BAT,
BALL &
BOUNDARY

BAT, BALL & BOUNDARY

A CRICKETER'S COMPANION

COMPILED BY
SHELLEY KLEIN

MICHAEL O'MARA BOOKS LIMITED

First published in Great Britain in 2001 by
Michael O'Mara Books Limited
9 Lion Yard
Tremadoc Road
London SW4 7NQ

A CIP catalogue record for this book is available from the British Library

ISBN 1-85479-527-9

1 3 5 7 9 10 8 6 4 2

Designed and typeset by Design 23
Printed and bound in Finland by WS Bookwell, Juva

Cricket. A sport at which contenders drive a ball with sticks or bats in opposition to each other.

SAMUEL JOHNSON
A Dictionary of the English Language, 1755

Acknowledgements

The publisher has made every effort to contact the copyright holders of material reproduced in this book, and wishes to apologize to those he has been unable to trace. Grateful acknowledgement is made for permission to reprint the following:

W. G. Grace by Bernard Darwin. Reprinted by permission of Gerald Duckworth & Co. Ltd.

Psmith in the City by P. G. Wodehouse. Reprinted by permission of A. P. Watt Ltd on behalf of The Trustees of the Wodehouse Estate.

The Cricket Match from *England, their England* by A. G. Macdonell. Reprinted by permission of Macmillan Publishers Ltd.

Cricket Country by Edmund Blunden (Copyright © Edmund Blunden 1944) by permission of PFD on behalf of the Estate of Mrs Claire Blunden.

Second Innings by Neville Cardus. Reprinted by kind permission of Margaret Hughes.

Farewell to Cricket by Don Bradman, published by Tom Thompson. Reprinted by permission of David Higham Associates.

Brightly Fades the Don by J. H. Fingleton. Reprinted by permission of HarperCollins Publishers Ltd.

Hill Cricket by Laurie Lee, from *Wisden Cricket Monthly*. Reprinted by kind permission of Wisden Cricket Magazines Ltd.

Military Matter by Simon Raven. Reprinted by permission of Curtis Brown on behalf of Simon Raven. Copyright © Simon Raven, 1982.

Cricket Wallah by Scyld Berry. Copyright 1982 Scyld Berry. Reprinted by permission of Hodder & Stoughton Ltd.

The Cricket Match by Hugh de Selincourt. First published by Jonathan Cape, 1924. Reprinted by kind permission of the estate of Hugh de Selincourt.

CONTENTS

GRACE BEFORE DINNER

ANONYMOUS (1878)

The Australians came down like a wolf on the fold,
The Marylebone cracks for a trifle were bowled,
Our Grace before dinner was very soon done,
And Grace after dinner did not get a run.

From W. G. GRACE

BY BERNARD DARWIN (1934)

W. G. Grace (1848–1915) stands for so much in the history of cricket that it is impossible to think of an anthology without him. He was the greatest cricketer in Victorian England, evolving the modern principles of batting and, as the famous bowler J. C. Shaw once said, 'I put the ball where I likes, but he puts it where he likes.' The following piece by the eminent sportswriter Bernard Darwin sums up Grace beautifully.

* * *

'W. G.,' SAID AN OLD FRIEND OF HIS, 'WAS JUST A GREAT BIG schoolboy in everything he did.' It would be difficult in a single sentence to come nearer to the clue to his character. He had all the schoolboy's love for elementary and boisterous jokes; his distaste for learning; his desperate and undisguised keenness; his guilelessness and his guile; his occasional pettishness and pettiness; his endless power of recovering his good spirits. To them may be added two qualities not as a rule to be found in schoolboys: a wonderful modesty and lack of vanity; an invariable kindness to those younger than himself, 'except', as one of his most devoted friends has observed, 'that he tried to chisel them out lbw.'.

If one had to choose a single epithet to describe him, it would, I think, be simple. 'I am not a psychologist,' he says in one of his books, and his estimate was doubtless accurate. He did not think very deeply or very subtly about anybody or anything; perhaps not even about cricket, although his knowledge of it was intuitively profound, his judgement of a cricketer unique. Of all the stories about him none is better known than his answer to a question as to how a particular stroke should be made: 'You put the bat against the ball.' It may be read in one of two slightly different senses, and in either it seems to reveal something of his character. Take it as a serious attempt to explain the whole secret of a stroke, an earnest endeavour to help the learner, and in that sense it shows his essential simplicity. Again it may be taken as a reflection on those who want to be too clever and abstruse, and I imagine that W. G. did not want people to be clever. He was too modest to have the contemptuous arrogance of the unlearned towards learning – that belongs to the lout, and he had no trace of it; but for his own part he liked best the other simple folk like himself. His interests were all of the open air. If people wanted to read books, no doubt they got pleasure from it, but it was a pleasure that he could not really understand. *Wisden*, yes, perhaps, to confirm a memory or refute an argument, or in winter as an earnest of the summer to come; but in a general way books were bad for cricket. 'How can you expect to make runs,' he said to one of the Gloucestershire side, 'when you are always reading?' and added, almost gratuitously, 'You don't catch me that way.' I have searched in vain for anyone who ever saw him take the risk, except in the case of a newspaper or a medical book in which he wanted to look up a point.

W. G. was not an intellectual man, and even as regards his own subject his was not an analytical brain, but by instinct or genius – call it what you will – he could form a judgement of a cricketer to which all others bowed. One who played much with him has given me two instances to which many more might, of course, be added. A schoolboy who had made innumerable runs for his school, and was generally regarded as an extraordinary cricketer, played in his first first-class match with W. G. and made a respectable score. Everybody crowded round the oracle to hear the verdict, and expected a favourable one. 'He'll never make a first-class cricketer.' That was all, and it turned out to be entirely true. Here is a converse example. When Mr Jessop first appeared for Gloucestershire, those who now realize that they ought to have known better were struck only by the more rough-hewn and bucolic aspects of his batting. 'What have you got here, old man?' they asked W. G. rather disparagingly. 'Ah, you wait and see what I've got here,' he answered with a touch of truculence, and went on to say that in a year or so this would be the finest hitter that had ever been seen. That this verdict also turned out true is hardly worth saying.

Moreover, if W. G. did not possess what is generally called cleverness, he had, within certain precise limits, a remarkable acuteness. He might not think deeply, but on his own subjects he could think quickly. 'A man must get up very early in the morning,' said the Game Chicken, 'to get the best of John Gully.' And many a cricketer might well have said it of W. G.. He had that sort of quickness of apprehension that may, without disrespect, perhaps be called cunning, and is often to be found, a little surprisingly, in those who seem at first sight simple-minded and almost rustic. He had plenty of shrewdness, too, in judging the qualities of men, so far as they interested him and came within his sphere. He might occasionally do ill-judged things in the excitement of the moment, but at the bottom of everything there was a good hard kernel of common sense.

We are told that when W. G. first appeared in first-class cricket he was shy, and we can picture him a tall, gawky, uneasy boy. He had not been to a public school; he came from a small country doctor's family; he had met few people except in his own country neighbourhood, and he suddenly found himself among those who had had a different sort of upbringing. It is no wonder that he was silent and uncomfortable. But fame and popularity are wonderful softeners of that agony of shyness, and, if he perhaps kept a little of it deep down inside him, there was no external trace of it. He was perfectly natural with all whom he met, and if he liked them he was soon friendly and hearty with them. He was helped by a wonderful unselfconsciousness. He seemed to take himself for granted, at once a supreme player of his game, and, off the field, as an ordinary person, and did not bother his head about what impression he made.

He was far better known by sight than any man in England. Long after his cricketing days were over he had only to pass through a village street in a motor-car for windows to be thrown up and fingers to be pointed, but he seemed, and really was, as nearly as possible unaware of it, unless perhaps his admirer was a small child, to whom he liked to wave his hand. This unselfconsciousness pervaded his whole existence. He had come, as has been said, from a home comparatively countrified and uncultivated; he kept, to some extent at least, its manners and its way of speech all his life. He mixed constantly with those who were, in a snobbish sense, his superiors and had other ways and other manners, and I do not believe that he ever gave such things a thought. He recognized different standards in the houses he stayed at, to the extent that there were some to which he ought to take his 'dancing–pumps', and that was all. He liked friendliness and cheerfulness wherever he met it; he was ready to give it himself, and never thought of anything else that could be demanded of him.

I do not know if I am right, but he gave me the impression that the one thing that would not go down with him was any elaborateness of manner, any too formal politeness. I remember a little scene on a golf course. I was playing with him in a foursome, and someone unintentionally drove into us from behind. W. G., always jealous of his rights in any game, resented it, but the driver of the ball apologized with extreme politeness, and surely all would now be over. But it was not. The more careful the apologies the less did W. G. let the poor man alone, until he made the rest of the foursome feel very uncomfortable. I thought then, and I think now, that if the offender had come up and said cheerfully, 'Doctor, I'm awfully sorry', and had even clapped him on the back, all would have been well, but he was the sort that cannot for the life of them clap people on the back, and nothing could atone.

It has been said that W. G. liked simple jokes, and if they were familiar ones of the 'old grouse in the gunroom type' so much the better. There seems to me something extremely characteristic about a story, very small and mild in itself, told by Mr C. E. Green in the *Memorial Biography*. Mr Green was the Master of the Essex Hounds, and had the hounds brought for W. G. to look at after breakfast. He liked the hounds, and he liked the Master's big grey horse, and Mr Green goes on, 'For years afterwards whenever we met he would sing out "How's my old grey horse?"' That is perhaps hardly worthy of the name of the joke, but, whatever it was, it was the kind of friendly chaff that pleased W. G.. He liked jokes to do with conviviality, for he was a convivial soul.

Essentially temperate in his everyday private life, he enjoyed good things on anything in the nature of an occasion; he had, as I fancy, a kind of Dickensian relish for good cheer, not merely the actual enjoyment of it but also the enjoyment of thinking and talking about it, and he combined with this, of course, a much greater practical capacity than Dickens ever had. A whole bottle of champagne was a mere nothing to him; having consumed it, he would go down on all fours and balance the bottle on the top of his head and rise to his feet again. Nothing could disturb that magnificent constitution, and those who hoped by a long and late sitting to shorten his innings next day often found themselves disappointed. His regular habit while cricketing was to drink one large whisky and soda, with a touch of angostura bitters, at lunch, and another when the day's play ended; this allowance he never varied or exceeded till the evening came, and, despite his huge frame, though he never dieted, he ate sparingly. His one attempt at a weight-reducing regimen was the drinking of cider. As he believed in a moderate amount of good drink, so he disbelieved strongly in tobacco. He had been brought up in a non-smoking family (though his brother Alfred became a backslider), and stuck to its tenets religiously all his life. It was an aphorism of his that 'you can get rid of drink, but you can never get rid of smoke'. He constantly proclaimed it was his own private belief, but he never made any attempt to put his team on any allowance of tobacco.

Mr A. J. Webbe tells me that he remembers at his mother's house in Eaton Square W. G. marching round the drawing-room after dinner, bearing the coal-scuttle on his head as a helmet, with the poker carried as a sword. It is an agreeable picture, and we may feel sure that W. G. was ready to go on marching just a little longer than anyone else, for his energy was as inexhaustible as his humour was childlike; he must be playing at something – billiards or cards, dancing or coal-scuttles, anything but sitting down. The simplicity of his humour often took, naturally enough, a practical direction. In one corner of his mind there probably lurked, all his life, amiable thoughts of booby traps and apple-pie beds, and he was even known in an exuberant moment on a golfing expedition to hurl rocks at a boat like another Polyphemus.

He carried his practical joking into the realms of cricket, as when, according to a well-known story, he caused the batsman to look up at the sky to see some imaginary birds, with the result that the poor innocent was blinded by the sun and promptly bowled. With this we come to one of the most difficult questions about W. G.: did he at all, and, if so, how far, overstep the line which, in a game, divides fair play from sharp practice? There is one preliminary thing to say, namely, that there is no absolute standard in these matters, and that standards differ with times and societies. The sportsmen of the early nineteenth century did, naturally and unblushingly, things that would be considered very unsportsmanlike nowadays. In those days everything was a 'match': each party must look after himself; it was play or pay, and the devil take the hindermost.

Anybody who reads the autobiography of the Squire, George Osbaldeston, will get an insight into the sporting morals of that day. 'A noble fellow, always straight,' said Mr Budd of the Squire; but he deliberately pulled a horse in order to get the better of those who in his estimation had overreached him, and, generally speaking, it was one of his guiding principles in all sports not to let the cat out of the bag. He never did what he thought a dishonourable thing, but he had a different standard of honour from our own. I believe that in W. G. was found something of a survival of this older tradition. He had his own notions of what was right and permissible, and I am convinced that he would never willingly have done anything contrary to them; the difficulty arose when other people did not think something permissible and he did. He would never have dreamed of purposely getting in the way of a fieldsman who might otherwise have caught him, but to shout cheerfully to that fieldsman, 'Miss it,' was – at any rate in a certain class of cricket – not merely within the law but rather a good joke.

The law was the law, though in his intense keenness he could not wholly rid himself of the idea that it was sometimes unjustly enforced against him; what the law allowed was allowable. It was always worth appealing; if the umpire thought a man was out lbw., it did not matter what the bowler thought. 'You weren't out, you know,' he was sometimes heard to say to a retiring batsman against whom he had appealed, and thought no shame to do so: everything was open and above-board; if the umpire decided you were out – and he sometimes decided wrong – that was all about it. He wanted desperately to get the other side out, and any fair way of doing so was justifiable; he never stooped to what he thought was a mean way. No man knew the law better, and it could seldom be said against him that he was wrong, but rather that he was too desperately right. Sometimes the fact that he had the reputation of wanting his pound of flesh caused him to be unjustly criticized when his claim was an entirely proper one.

There was a certain match between Gloucestershire and Sussex, in which, at the end of the second innings of Sussex, the Sussex total for two innings was exactly equal to that of Gloucestershire's one innings, and there were left some eleven or eleven and a half minutes of time. Ten minutes' interval left a minute or so in which to get the one run for a ten-wicket victory. W. G. properly declared that Gloucestershire should go in. Sussex to some extent seemed to

have demurred on the ground that there was not time for an over.
However, they went out to field. Ranji had changed into ordinary
clothes, and W. G. went out to field as substitute for him. Tate
bowled the one over to Jessop, and nothing could be done with
three balls. The fourth was pushed gently towards W. G. at point,
and the run gained almost before he had had time to stoop. It is a
subject for irreverent speculation what would have happened if the
batsmen had been caught in two minds in the middle of the pitch.
Would that ball have gone straight to the wicketkeeper or is it
possible that there would have been an overthrow?

In the matter of enforcing rules – and on this particular
occasion W. G. was clearly in the right – the manner of his
bringing up ought always to be remembered. His early cricket had
been played with a father and three elder brothers who were going
to stand no nonsense from the younger ones. The boy was taught
to behave himself, and this meant, amongst other things, to stick to
the rules. It was natural enough that when he grew older he
expected other players to behave themselves too. It may be said
that he did not sufficiently distinguish between big points and
small ones, but the answer is that, where cricket was concerned,
there was for W. G. no such thing as a small point. It might seem
trivial to more easy-going or more flexibly minded persons; never
to him; and if things were not, as he thought, just right, he came
out bluntly and impetuously with his opinion.

His elder brothers had not had any excessive consideration for
his young feelings, and it may be that, on the field of play, he had
not a great deal of consideration for other people's. No doubt
W. G. at point could be a little trying to the highly-strung batsman.
'These Graces chatter so,' said Sir Timothy O'Brien, who did not
suffer things gladly, and with W. G. and E. M. both fielding close to
the wicket, and neither having any too tender a regard for the
batsman, perfect concentration of mind was difficult to attain. He
appealed freely himself when he was bowling, and, subject to
discipline, he approved of other members of his side appealing too.
'Why didn't you appeal, Fred?' he snapped at the bowler after the
over. 'Well, sir,' said Roberts, 'I looked towards you at the time.'

A young Gloucestershire amateur, not the bowler, once got a
formidable Australian stonewaller given out, and there was some
little unpleasantness. He asked W. G. if he had been right to
appeal. 'Right?' was the answer. 'I should think you were right.
Why, if you hadn't, we might never have got him out.' One small
story on this point may be allowed, because it is so agreeably
typical of all the parties concerned. F. S. Jackson, as it is still
natural to call him, was playing for Yorkshire against

Gloucestershire in his first season of county cricket. E. M. stood a minimum of yards away at point, W. G. almost equally near on the leg side, and they 'chattered' across their victim in their best manner. Lord Hawke, the Yorkshire captain, made some excuse to come on the field and said to the young batsman, 'Are those two old beggars trying to bustle you?' 'I don't know,' was the answer, 'but anyhow, they can't.'

To W. G., cricket, being a game, was a vehicle for a practical rough-and-tumble humour. Possibly he did not appreciate it so whole-heartedly when the joke was turned against himself, but that is an amiable weakness of practical jokers all the world over. He never let it seriously discompose him as E. M. sometimes did. Once upon a time, so it is alleged, E. M. was batting to S. M. J. Woods and was hit upon his, as ever, ungloved hand. He dropped his bat and shook his fingers in pain, whereat somebody in the crowd guffawed and made some audible remark. 'I can't stand that, Sammy,' he cried, and ran to the boundary. 'Who said that?' he asked the crowd. 'There he is, Doctor,' answered the crowd, indicating a youthful and now terrified delinquent trying to escape, whereupon the coroner plunged in among the spectators in a pursuit which was, let us hope, unsuccessful.

Cricket with W. G. was never a game to be played in deathly silence. His voice was often to be heard on the field, in exhortation or comment. The sound of his 'Keep your arm up, Fred' to one of his bowlers was familiar to the Gloucestershire side and its adversaries. Even E. M. did not escape criticism if it was thought that he ought to have got a catch. The less serious the match, the greater licence of humour did W. G. allow himself. One of the most often demanded of Arthur Croome's stories related to some village match in which E. M. was bowling and W. G. fielding at point. There came a steady stream of appeals from E. M., all steadily refused. Then said W. G. confidentially to the umpire, 'Never mind my brother, he's always appealing. Now when I appeal it *is* out.' An over or two passed, and then came, 'How's that?'

from point, and out went the batsman. First-class umpires can neither be bustled nor bamboozled, but in any case W. G. would not have done that in a big match; the joke was suited to the occasion.

It is idle to deny, I suppose, that he led umpires rather a hard life; some of them may have been frightened of giving him out, but if he ever intimidated them it was certainly not of malice aforethought; it was rather that irrepressibly keen boy in him that had never quite grown up and would break out now and then on the impulse of the moment. A boy naturally and properly thinks the umpire a beast who gives him out, and if there was a Peter Pan in the world it was Dr W. G. Grace. On the whole it was fortunate for him that umpires are not a revengeful race; indeed they probably stood so much in awe of him as to give him sometimes the benefit of the doubt. I am afraid of retelling old stories, but here is one new at any rate to me. Gloucestershire were playing Essex, and when he had made three or four W. G. was, in the general estimation of both sides, caught and bowled by Mead. He stoutly declared it was a bump-ball, and, after some palaver, he went on batting. In due course Kortright knocked his middle and leg stumps down, and, as the Old Man made ready to depart, exclaimed, 'What, are you going? There's still one standing.' W. G. said he had never been so insulted in his life, 'but', as the Gloucestershire narrator added, 'he'd made enough runs to win the match.'

More and more as time went on these little eccentricities were accepted, with a rueful and affectionate smile, as 'pretty Fanny's ways'. Nevertheless a burning anxiety to enforce the law in one direction only must lead to disputes and, more rarely, to what is vulgarly known as a jolly row. Yet the rows passed. If W. G. did not always apologize, neither did he ever bear malice; he forgot, and others, as far as there was anything to forgive, forgave. Some men, we know, cannot look over the hedge; W. G. was so essentially lovable that he could steal a horse now and then. As at cricket, so at golf. He would employ by way of a highly effective joke, certain devices not usually reckoned orthodox. It is recorded of him in a certain foursome competition that, finding one of his adversaries driving too far and too straight for his liking, he told him funny stories (despite the mild protests of his own partner) until all the drives ended in the gorse or the heather.

One of W. G.'s most engaging qualities, upon which all who knew him are agreed, was his unvarying kindness to young cricketers. He encouraged and advised them, sympathized with them in good or evil fortune, looked after them off the field, and saw that they did not feel lonely or shy. Save only when they gave themselves airs they were sure of a friendly and cheering word. When at his jubilee dinner this trait of his was mentioned, W. G. said that he was afraid he had not always been so kind, and told the story of a luckless colt whom he had hit out of the ground four times running and so ended his career once and for all. But that was in the way of business, and then he could be, as was his bounden duty, the most ruthless of killers.

Mr Neville Cardus has told admirably the story, as told to him, of a young fast bowler who, on his first appearance for the Players, had the lash of the Doctor's bat laid on with so cruel a precision that when he went to bed at night he cried like a child. Yet, even in the heat of conflict, W. G. could do the kindliest and most generous things. Mr George Brann when quite a young man had made 99 against Gloucestershire. W. G. approached H. V. Page, the bowler, and told him to give the young batsman any kind of ball that he wanted. The bowler asked how he would like it. Mr Brann modestly expressed a preference for a long hop on the off, had it served up to him, and pulled it on to his wicket. Virtue that time was more than its own reward, and so it was when he gave Abel, who had made 96, a slow full-pitch to leg, and saw the ball neatly deposited in the hands of square-leg, fielding deep on the boundary. It has been alleged in this case that, having first promised the full pitch, he then privily moved the fieldsman, but I do not believe it. The humour of such a proceeding would have appealed to him, but he would have resisted it.

W. G.'s kindness to the young consisted not so much in what he said as in what he made them feel. A good innings might earn no more than, 'Well played, young 'un', but the recipient of those words touched the stars with uplifted head. To one who had been summarily bowled, 'Rather you had that one than I' brought balm beyond belief. Mr Jessop has told me of his first match for Gloucestershire. He had been getting a great many wickets in second-class cricket and was reasonably complacent. He was put on first to bowl against Lancashire, against A. C. McLaren and Albert Ward, and one of them was soon missed off him at the wicket. He bowled and bowled; he nearly bowled his heart out, and the reward of thirty-four overs or so was one wicket – lbw.. He was feeling like a pricked bubble, utterly depressed, and then, when he got into the

dressing-room W. G. said to him, 'Well bowled, young 'un.'
Instantly the air was full of trumpets, the whole world rosy and
golden, and he thought that, after all, he might play for
Gloucestershire again. He did tolerably well in another match or
so, and W. G. said that he could give him a place in one of the two
matches at Cheltenham – which would he like? Not unnaturally he
chose the first, in the hopes that he might earn his place in the
second, and there was never any more doubt.

W. G. did not, as a rule try to teach his young men. This was
natural enough in Mr Jessop's case, for he saw that there was a
natural genius, far more likely to be spoiled than improved; but,
generally speaking, it was his practice to cheer, to sympathize but to
let alone, leaving the young man to work out his own salvation. He
was always particular in noting and praising good fielding, and if
the catch was off his own bowling the praise was not the less
hearty. Though he had himself profited by Uncle Pocock, he had
no great belief in coaching, and thought too much of it could do a
young cricketer great harm. He carried out this principle in playing
with his own sons when they were children. His coaching did not
go far beyond seizing the bat and saying, 'This is the way to do it.'

That he was worshipped by all the young amateurs who played
under his banner is certain. There is a touching little story of
Arthur Croome's, of how three young players on the
Gloucestershire side, having, as they thought, been rather cavalierly
treated, conspired to call W. G. 'Dr Grace' for a short while, and
how he worried himself and appealed to other people and plucked
his beard, wondering and wondering how he had hurt their
feelings. Of course they relented, and were fonder of him than
ever. Whether the professional had quite the same feeling of
adoration is doubtful. He could be a martinet, and treated them on
occasions a little brusquely. While he was friendly, he had no
notion of their being familiar with him. Perhaps, too, there was a
slight, underlying tradition of hostility in the professional ranks, in
that they thought he had made more money out of cricket than

they had done and yet they were not amateurs. They all had
naturally a vast respect for his powers, and many of them, such as
Alfred Shaw, Shrewsbury, Abel and Murch, had a real affection for
him as well. It was the 'family circle' of the Gloucestershire
amateurs that had the warmest feeling of all, but it is difficult for
even the most casual acquaintance not to be conscious of his
lovableness and almost to dare to love him.

A more truly modest game-player than W. G. could not be
found. He knew how good he was, of course, but he never
condescended or patronized, and never spoke of his own
achievements. Occasionally, though not often, he would talk about
old times, but then not of himself but of the cricketers of his
youthful prime. Fred, always remembered with affectionate
admiration, had done this or that, or George Freeman had been,
on the whole, the finest fast bowler against whom he had ever
played. 'He used to get you here,' he would say, pointing to the
inside of his thigh, 'and the ball felt as if it was going on there,
going round and round.' . . .

In writing a personal sketch of a famous man, it is usual to say
something of his appearance. In the case of W. G. as a cricketer,
this must be unnecessary. We all know the vast bulk, the black
beard in later years streaked with grey, the red and yellow cap.
There is, however, another aspect of him that is not familiar –
W. G. as a private person in mufti, and not a flannelled general on
the battlefield. One proud and lucky man possesses a photograph,
which will remain unique, since the plate is broken. It shows W. G.
in his everyday clothes just before he is going into the pavilion to
change. It is the first morning of the deciding Test Match at the
Oval in 1896. He has been looking at the wicket, and discussing
with F. S. Jackson what is to be done if he wins the toss. On his
head is one of those square felt hats which we generally associate
with farmers. He wears a black tail-coat and waist-coat, built on
easy-going lines with an expanse of watch-chain, dark trousers, a
little baggy at the knee, and boots made for muddy lanes. In one

hand is a solid blackthorn stick with a silver band round it. Future generations who see that photograph will protest that this cannot be a mighty athlete about to lead the chosen of England to victory. It must be, they will say, a jovial middle-aged doctor discussing the price of oats with a patient or neighbour that he had met in the market-place. The man in that picture is W. G., but it is the one we do not know, the country doctor who had followed his father's business, who could never quite understand why no one of his three sons wanted to be a country doctor too.

The W. G. that we know best is not merely a celebrity but the central figure in a cricketing mythology. The stories about him are endless, and this can hardly be explained by the fact that he was the best of all cricketers, that he looked the part of a Colossus, and had an amusing way of saying characteristic things. There have been many other mighty players if admittedly below him; yet the sum of the stories about them all is, by comparison, negligible. Many of them, though very famous in their day, live for us now only as minor personages in the W. G. legend; they are remembered because they come incidentally into stories about him. In point of his personality, as it will be handed on by tradition for years to come, he towers as high above them as he towered above them in stature when he was alive. If this is not greatness, it is something for which it is hard to find another name. May we not say that, with all his limitations, his one-sidedness, his simplicity, W. G. possessed in an obscure and unconscious way some of the qualities of a great man?

From HOURS OF IDLENESS

BY LORD BYRON (1807)

George Gordon Byron (1788–1824) was born in London and
during his lifetime wrote some of the most memorable poetry in
the English language. *Hours of Idleness* was his first published
volume of verse. He was educated at Harrow where the following
extract is set.

* * *

High through those elms, with hoary branches crown'd,
Fair Ida's bower adorns the landscape round;
There Science, from her favour'd seat, surveys
The vale where rural Nature claims her praise;
To her awhile resigns her youthful train,
Who move in joy, and dance along the plain;
In scatter'd groups each favour'd haunt pursue,
Repeat old pastimes, and discover new;
Flush'd with his rays beneath the noontide sun,
In rival bands, between the wickets run,
Drive o'er the sward the ball with active force,
Or chase with nimble feet its rapid course.

Friend of my heart, and foremost of the list
Of those with whom I lived supremely blest,
Oft have we drained the font of ancient lore;
Though drinking deeply, thirsting still the more,
Yet, when confinement's lingering hour was done,
Our sports, our studies, and our souls were one:
Together we impelled the flying ball;
Together waited in our tutor's hall;
Together joined in cricket's manly toil,
Or shared the produce of the river's spoil;
Or, plunging from the green declining shore,
Our pliant limbs the buoyant billows bore;
In every element, unchanged, the same,
All, all that brothers should be, but the name.

From OUR VILLAGE

BY MARY RUSSELL MITFORD (1824)

Mary Russell Mitford (1787–1855) is best remembered for her five-volume collection of essays, 'Our Village – sketches of rural life, character, and scenery', which were first published in *The Lady's Magazine*. The scene of most of her pieces is Three Mile Cross, near Reading, and I think you'll agree when I say that she succeeds admirably when it comes to capturing the charm of village cricket.

* * *

FOR THE LAST THREE WEEKS OUR VILLAGE HAS BEEN IN A STATE OF great excitement, occasioned by a challenge from our north-western neighbours, the men of B., to contend with us at cricket. Now, we have not been much in the habit of playing matches. Three or four years ago, indeed, we encountered the men of S., our neighbours south-by-east, with a sort of doubtful success, beating them on our own ground, whilst they in the second match returned the compliment on theirs. This discouraged us. Then an unnatural coalition between a high-church curate and an evangelical gentleman farmer drove our lads from the Sunday-evening practice, which, as it did not begin before both services were concluded, and as it tended to keep the young men from the ale-house, our magistrates had winked at, if not encouraged. The sport, therefore, had languished until the present season, when under another change of circumstance the spirit began to revive.

Half-a-dozen fine active lads, of influence amongst their comrades, grew into men and yearned for cricket; an enterprising publican gave a set of ribands: his rival, mine host of the Rose, an outdoer by profession, gave two; and the clergyman and his lay ally, both well-disposed and good-natured men, gratified by the submission to the authority, and finding, perhaps, that no great good resulted from the substitution of public houses for out-of-door diversions, relaxed. In short, the practice recommenced, and the hill was again alive with men and boys, and innocent merriment; but farther than the riband matches amongst ourselves nobody dreamed of going, till this challenge – we were modest, and doubted our own strength. The B. people, on the other hand, must have been braggers born, a whole parish of gasconaders. Never was such boasting! such crowing! such ostentatious display of practice! such mutual compliments from man to man – bowler to batter, batter to bowler! It was a wonder they did not challenge all England. It must be confessed that we were a little astounded; yet we firmly resolved not to decline the combat; and one of the most spirited of the new growth, William Grey by name, took up the glove in a style of manly courtesy, that would have done honour to a knight in the days of chivalry. 'We were not professed players,' he said, 'being little better than schoolboys, and scarcely older; but, since they had done us the honour to challenge us, we would try our strength. It would be no discredit to be beaten by such a field.'

Having accepted the wager of battle, our champion began forthwith to collect his forces. William Grey is himself one of the finest youths that one shall see – tall, active, slender and yet strong, with a piercing eye full of sagacity, and a smile full of good humour – a farmer's son by station, and used to hard work as farmers' sons are now, liked by everybody, and admitted to be an excellent cricketer. He immediately set forth to muster his men, remembering with great complacency that Samuel Long, a bowler *comme il y en a peu*, the very man who had knocked down nine wickets, had beaten us, bowled us out at the fatal return match some years ago at S., had luckily, in a remove of a quarter of a mile last Ladyday, crossed the boundaries of his old parish, and actually belonged to us. Here was a stroke of good fortune! Our captain applied to him instantly; and he agreed at a word. Indeed, Samuel Long is a very civilized person. He is a middle-aged man, who

looks rather old amongst our young lads, and whose thickness and
breadth give no token of remarkable activity; but he is very active,
and so steady a player! so safe! We had half gained the match when
we had secured him. He is a man of substance, too, in every way;
owns one cow, two donkeys, six pigs, and geese and ducks beyond
count – dresses like a farmer, and owes no man a shilling – and all
this from pure industry, sheer day-labour. Note that your good
cricketer is commonly the most industrious man in the parish; the
habits that make him such are precisely those which make a good
workman – steadiness, sobriety, and activity. Samuel Long might
pass for the *beau ideal* of the two characters. Happy were we to
possess him!

Then we had another piece of good luck. James Brown, a
journeyman blacksmith and a native, who, being of rambling
disposition, had roamed from place to place for half-a-dozen years,
had just returned to settle with his brother at another corner of
our village, bringing with him a prodigious reputation in cricket
and in gallantry – the gay Lothario of the neighbourhood. He is
said to have made more conquests in love and in cricket than any
blacksmith in the country . . .

That Sunday evening's practice (for Monday was the important
day) was a period of great anxiety, and, to say the truth, of great
pleasure. There is something strangely delightful in the innocent
spirit of party. To be one of a numerous body, to be authorized to
say *we*, to have a rightful interest in triumph or defeat, is gratifying
at once to social feeling and to personal pride. There was not a ten-
year-old urchin, or a septuagenary woman in the parish, who did
not feel an additional importance, a reflected consequence, in
speaking of 'our side'. An election interests in the same way; but
that feeling is less pure. Money is there, and hatred, and politics,
and lies. Oh, to be a voter, or a voter's wife, comes nothing near
the genuine and hearty sympathy of belonging to a parish,
breathing the same air, looking on the same trees, listening to the
same nightingales! Talk of a patriotic elector! Give me a parochial

patriot, a man who loves his parish! Even we, the female partisans, may partake the common ardour. I am sure I did. I never, though tolerably eager and enthusiastic at all times, remember being in a more delicious state of excitement than on the eve of that battle. Our hopes waxed stronger and stronger. Those of our players who were present were excellent . . .

On calling over our roll, Brown was missing . . . Charles Groven – the universal scout and messenger of the village, a man who will run half-a-dozen miles for a pint of beer, who does errands for the very love of the trade, who, if he had been a lord, would have been an ambassador – was instantly despatched to summon the truant. His report spread general consternation. Brown had set off at four o'clock in the morning to play a cricket match at M., a little town twelve miles off, which had been his last residence. Here was desertion! Here was treachery! Here was treachery against that goodly state, our parish! To send James Brown to Coventry was the immediate resolution; but even that seemed too light a punishment for such delinquency. Then how we cried him down! At ten on Sunday night (for the rascal had actually practised with us, and never said a word of his intended disloyalty) he was our faithful mate, and the best player (take him for all in all) of the eleven. At ten in the morning he had run away, and we were well rid of him. . . . But I have since learned the secret history of the offence (if we could know the secret histories of all offences, how much better the world would seem than it does now!) and really my wrath is much abated. It was a piece of gallantry, of devotion to the sex, or rather a chivalrous obedience to one chosen fair. I must tell my readers the story.

Mary Allen, the prettiest girl of M., had, it seems, revenged upon our blacksmith the numberless inconsistencies of which he stood accused. He was in love over head and ears, but the nymph was cruel. She said no, and no, and no, and poor Brown, three times rejected, at last resolved to leave the place, partly in despair, and partly in that hope which often mingles strangely with a lover's despair, the hope that when he was gone he should be missed. He came home to his brother's accordingly; but for five weeks he heard nothing from or of the inexorable Mary, and was glad to beguile his own 'vexing thoughts' by endeavouring to create in his mind an artificial and factitious interest in our cricket match – all unimportant as such a trifle must have seemed to a man in love. Poor James, however, is a social and warm-hearted person, not likely to resist a contagious sympathy. As the time for the play advanced, the interest which he had at first affected became genuine and sincere: and he was really, when he left the ground on Sunday night, almost as enthusiastically absorbed in the event of the next day as Joel Brent himself. He little foresaw the new and delightful interest which awaited him at home, where, on the moment of his arrival, his sister-in-law and confidante presented him with a billet from the lady of his heart. It had, with the usual delay of letters sent by private hands in that rank of life, loitered on the road, in a degree inconceivable to those who are accustomed to the punctual speed of the post, and had taken ten days for its twelve miles' journey. Have my readers any wish to see this *billet-doux*? I can show them (but in strict confidence) a literal copy. It was addressed,

> 'For mistur jem browne
> > 'blaxmith by
> > > 'S.'

The inside ran thus: 'Mistur browne this is to Inform you that oure parish plays bramley men next Monday is a week, i think we shall lose without yew. From you humbell servant to command
> > > > Mary Allen.'

Was there ever a prettier relenting? a summons more flattering, more delicate, more irresistible? The precious epistle was undated; but, having ascertained who brought it, and found, by cross-examining the messenger, that the Monday in question was the

very next day, we were not
surprised to find that *Mistur
browne* forgot his
engagement to us, forgot all
but Mary and Mary's letter,
and set off at four o'clock
the next morning to walk
twelve miles and play for
her parish, and in her sight.
Really we must not send
James Brown to Coventry –
must we? Though if, as his
sister-in-law tells our damsel
Harriet he hopes to do, he
should bring the fair Mary
home as his bride, he will
not greatly care how little we
say to him. But he must not
be sent to Coventry – True-
love forbid!

At last we were all
assembled, and marched
down to H. common, the
appointed ground, which, though in our dominions according to
the maps, was the constant practising place of our opponents, and
terra incognita to us. We found our adversaries on the ground as we
expected, for our various delays had hindered us from taking the
field so early as we wished; and, as soon as we had settled all
preliminaries, the match began. But alas! I have been so long
settling my preliminaries, that I have left myself no room for the
detail of our victory, and must squeeze the account of our grand
achievements into as little compass as Cowley, when he crammed
the names of eleven of his mistresses into the narrow space of four
eight-syllable lines.

They began the warfare – those boastful men of B. And what think you, gentle reader, was the amount of the innings! These challengers – the famous eleven – how many did they get? Think! imagine! guess! – You cannot? – Well! – they got twenty-two, or, rather, they got twenty; for two of theirs were short notches, and would never have been allowed, only that, seeing what they were made of, we and our umpires were not particular. – They should have had twenty more if they had chosen to claim them. Oh, how well we fielded! and how well we bowled! our good play had quite as much to do with their miserable failure as their bad. Samuel Long is a slow bowler, George Simmons a fast one, and the change from Long's lobbing to Simmons's fast balls posed them completely. Poor simpletons! they were always wrong, expecting the slow for the quick and the quick for the slow. Well, we went in. And what were our innings? Guess again! – guess! A hundred and sixty-nine! in spite of soaking showers, and wretched ground, where the ball would not run a yard, we headed them by a hundred and forty-seven; and then they gave in, as well they might. William Grey pressed them much to try another innings. 'There was so much chance', as he courteously observed, 'in cricket, that advantageous as our position seemed, we might, very possibly, be overtaken. The B. men had better try.' But they were beaten sulky, and would not move – to my great disappointment; I wanted to prolong the pleasure of success. What a glorious sensation it is to be for five hours together – winning – winning! always feeling what a whist-player feels when he takes up four honours, seven trumps! Who would think that a little bit of leather, and two pieces of wood, had such a delightful and delighting power!

From Book of Sports and Mirror of Life

by Pierce Egan (1832)

Here lies, bowl'd out by DEATH's unerring ball,
A CRICKETER renowned, by name JOHN SMALL;
But though his name was *small*, yet *great* his fame,
For nobly did he play the 'noble game'.
His *life* was like his *innings* – long and good;
Full ninety summers he had DEATH withstood,
At length the *ninetieth* winter came – when (Fate
Not leaving him one solitary *mate*)
This last of *Hambledonians*, old JOHN SMALL,
Gave up his BAT and BALL – his LEATHER, *wax* and *all*.

From THE YOUNG CRICKETER'S TUTOR

BY JOHN NYREN

(EDITED BY CHARLES COWDEN CLARKE, 1833)

John Nyren (1764–1837) was, in his time, a famous cricketer, pub landlord and, later in life, became a well-known chronicler of all things cricket. He belonged to the Hambledon Cricket Club (founded circa 1750) and was a left-handed batsman of average ability, but a fine field at point and mid-wicket. Andrew Lang, the Scottish scholar renowned for his collections of fairy tales, described Nyren as the 'delightful Herodotus of the Early Historic Period of Cricket'.

* * *

THE NEXT PLAYER I SHALL NAME IS JAMES AYLWARD. HIS FATHER was a farmer. After he had played with the club [Hambledon] for a few years, Sir Horace got him away from us, and made him his bailiff, I think, or some such officer; I remember, however, he was but ill qualified for his post. Aylward was a left-handed batter, and one of the safest hitters I ever knew in the club. He once stayed in two whole days, and upon that occasion got the highest number of runs that had ever been gained by any member – *one hundred and sixty-seven*! Jemmy was not a good fieldsman, neither was he remarkably active. After he had left us, to go down to live with Sir Horace, he played against us, but never, to my recollection, with any advantage to his new associates – the Hambledonians were almost always too strong for their opponents. He was introduced to the club by Tom Taylor, and Tom's anxiety upon the occasion,

that his friend should do credit to his recommendation, was
curiously conspicuous. Aylward was a stout, well-made man,
standing about five feet nine inches; not very light about the limbs,
indeed he was rather clumsy. He would sometimes affect a little
grandeur of manner, and once got laughed at by the whole ground
for calling for a lemon to be brought to him when he had been in
but a little while. It was thought a piece of finnikiness by those
simple and homely yeomen.

And now for those anointed clod-stumpers, the Walkers, Tom
and Harry. Never sure came two such unadulterated rustics into a
civilized community. How strongly are the figures of the men (of
Tom's in particular) brought to my mind when they first presented
themselves to the club, upon Windmill-Down. Tom's hard,
ungainly, scrag-of-mutton frame; wilted, apple-john face (he always
looked twenty years older than he really was), his long spider legs,
as thick at the ankles as at the hips and perfectly straight all the
way down – for the embellishment of a calf in Tom's leg Dame
Nature had considered would be but a wanton superfluity. Tom
was the driest and most rigid-limbed chap I ever knew; his skin was
like the rind of an old oak, and as sapless. I have seen his knuckles
handsomely knocked about from Harris's bowling; but never saw
any blood upon his hands – you might just as well attempt to
phlebotomize a mummy. This rigidity of muscle (or rather I should
say of tendon, for muscle was another ingredient economized in
the process of Tom's configuration) – this rigidity, I say, was carried
into every motion. He moved like the rude machinery of a steam-
engine in the infancy of construction, and when he ran, every
member seemed ready to fly to the four winds. He toiled like a tar
on horseback.

The uncouth actions of these men furnished us, who prided
ourselves upon a certain grace in movement and finished air, with
an everlasting fund of amusement, and for some time they took no
great fancy to me, because I used to worry, and tell them they
could not play. They were, however, good hands when they first

came among us, and had evidently received most excellent instruction; but after they had derived the advantage of first-rate practice, they became most admirable batters, and were the trustiest fellows (particularly Tom) in cases of emergency or difficulty. They were devilish troublesome customers to get out. I have very frequently known Tom to go in first, and remain to the very last man. He was the coolest, the most imperturbable fellow in existence: it used to be said of him that he had no nerves at all. Whether he was only practising, or whether he knew that the game was in a critical state, and that much depended upon his play, he was the same phlegmatic, unmoved man – he was the Washington of cricketers. Neither he nor his brother was active, yet both were effective fieldsmen. Upon one occasion, on the Mary-le-bone grounds, I remember Tom going in first, and Lord Frederick Beauclerk giving him the first four balls, all of an excellent length. First four or last four made no difference to Tom – he was always the same cool, collected fellow. Every ball he dropped down just before his bat. Off went his lordship's white hat – dash upon the ground (his constant action when disappointed) – calling him at the same time 'a confounded old beast'. – 'I doan't care what ee zays,' said Tom, when one close by asked if he had heard Lord Frederick call him 'an old beast'. No, no; Tom was not the man to be flustered.

About a couple of years after Walker had been with us, he began the system of throwing instead of bowling, now so much the fashion. At that time it was esteemed foul play, and so it was decided by a council of the Hambledon Club which was called for the purpose. The first I recollect seeing revive the custom was Wills, a Sussex man. I am decidedly of the opinion, that if it be not stopped altogether, the character of the game will become changed. I should hope that such powerful and efficient members of the Mary-le-bone Club as Mr Ward, &c., will determine, not only to discountenance, but wholly and finally to suppress it; and instead, to foster and give every encouragement to genuine, bona fide bowlers – men with a fine delivery.

I never thought much of Tom's bowling; indeed the bowling of that time was so supereminent that he was not looked upon as a bowler – even for a change. He afterwards, however, greatly improved; and what with his thorough knowledge of the game, his crafty manner (for he was one of the most fox-headed fellows I ever saw), and his quickness in seizing every advantage, he was of considerable service to his party, but he never was a first-rate bowler. He was a right- and Harry a left-handed batter, and both were valuable men. They came from Thursley, near Hindhead; they and their father were farmers, and their land lay near to the Devil's Punch-bowl.

The next in succession will be John Wells, the Beldhams, Harris, and Freemantle.

Shortly after the Walkers had joined us, John Wells became a member of the Hambledon Club. John lived at Farnham, in Surrey, and was, if I recollect, a baker by trade. He was a short, thick, well-set man; in make like a cob-horse, proportionately strong, active, and laborious. As a bowler he had a very good delivery; he was also a good general field, and a steady batter – in short, an excellent 'servant of all work'; and, like those misused Gibeonites ('hewers of wood and drawers of water'), he was never spared when a wear-and-tear post was to be occupied. In cricket, as in the graver pursuits in life, the willing workman is ever spurred; he may perform labours of supererogation, and his assiduity meets at best with 'mouth honour': let him, however, but relax his muscles –

let him but shorten his career to the speed of his fellows, and he instantly sinks below them in the estimation of his employers. Whether in this case the feeling arise from envy or not, it is hard to decide; assuredly, however, in very many instances, the mill-horse-grinder in the track of duty is acknowledged with greeting, while extra merit 'goes out sighing'. John Wells possessed all the requisites for making a thoroughly useful cricketer; and, in his general deportment, he was endowed with those qualities which render man useful to society as well as happy in himself. He was a creature of a transparent and unflawed integrity – plain, simple, and candid; uncompromising, yet courteous; civil and deferential, yet no cringer. He always went by the title of 'Honest John Wells', and as long as I knew him he never forfeited the character he had gained. Little more need be added respecting his merits as a player, for he must be fresh in the memory of all who have been accustomed to see the best playing; suffice to say that, in addition to his level merits as a general cricketer, he was esteemed to possess an excellent judgement of the game, and in questions that were frequently mooted his opinion would be appealed to.

The Beldhams, George and William, come next in succession, brothers, and both farmers. They also, with Wells, came from Farnham. George was what would be called a fine player; a good batter, and generally competent to fill the different posts in the game; but, as he attended the club a few times only during my stay in it, I am unable to discriminate or speak pointedly to his merits. Upon turning, however, to his brother William, we come to the finest batter of his own, or perhaps of any age. William Beldham was a close-set, active man, standing about five feet eight inches and a half. He had light-coloured hair, a fair complexion, and handsome as well as intelligent features. We used to call him 'Silver Billy'. No one within my recollection could stop a ball better, or make more brilliant hits all over the ground. Wherever the ball was bowled, there she was hit away, and in the most severe, venomous style. Besides this, he was so remarkably safe a player; he was safer than the Bank, for no mortal ever thought of doubting Beldham's stability. He received his instructions from a gingerbread baker at Farnham, of the name of Harry Hall. I once played against Hall, and found him a very fair hand, yet nothing remarkable; he knew the principles of the game, yet, like many of inferior merit in performance, he made nevertheless an excellent tutor. He was a slow bowler, and a pretty good one. He had a peculiar habit of bringing his hand from behind his back immediately previous to his delivering the ball – a trick no doubt perplexing enough to an inexperienced batter. In his peripatetic lectures to the young students, Hall perpetually enforced the principle of keeping the *left* elbow well up (this charge was of course delivered to the *right*-handed hitters), and excellent instruction it was; for if you do keep that elbow well up, and your bat also upright (in stopping *a length ball*), you will not fail to keep the balls *down*; and, vice versa, lower your elbow, and your balls will infallibly mount when you strike them.

Beldham was quite a young man when he joined the Hambledon Club; and even in that stage of his playing I hardly ever saw a man with a finer command of his bat; but, with the instruction and advice of the old heads superadded, he rapidly attained to the extraordinary accomplishment of being the finest player that has appeared within the latitude of more than half a century. There can be no exception against his batting, or the severity of his hitting. He would get in at the balls, and hit them away in a gallant style; yet, in this single feat, I think I have known him excelled; but when he could cut them at the point of the bat he was in his glory; and upon my life, their speed was as the speed of thought. One of the most beautiful sights that can be imagined, and which would have delighted an artist, was to see him make himself up to hit a ball. It was the *beau ideal* of grace, animation, and concentrated energy. In this peculiar exhibition of elegance with vigour, the nearest approach to him, I think, was Lord Frederick Beauclerk. Upon one occasion at Mary-le-bone, I remember these two admirable batters being in together, and though Beldham was then verging towards his climacteric, yet both were excited to a competition, and the display of talent that was exhibited between them that day was the most interesting sight of its kind I ever witnessed. I should not forget, among his other excellences, to mention that Beldham was one of the best judges of a short run I ever knew; add to which, that he possessed a generally good knowledge of the game.

Hitherto I have spoken only of his batting. In this department alone, he had talent enough to make a dozen ordinary cricketers, but as a general fieldsman there were few better; he could take any post in the field, and do himself credit in it: latterly he usually chose the place of slip. But Beldham was a good change bowler too; he delivered his balls high, and they got up well. His pace was a moderate one, yet bordering upon the quick. His principal fault in this department was that he would often give a toss; taking him, however, as a change bowler, he was one of the best. He would very quickly discover what a hitter could do, and what he could not do, and arrange his bowling accordingly. Finally, although his balls were commonly to the length, he was much better calculated for a change than to be continued a considerable length of time. One of the finest treats in cricketing that I remember, was to see this admirable man in, with the beautiful bowling of Harris.

Having finished with the best batter of his own, or, perhaps, of any age – Beldham – we proceed to the very best bowler; a bowler who, between any one and himself, comparison must fail. David Harris was, I believe, born, at all events he lived, at Odiham, in Hampshire; he was by trade a potter. He was a muscular, bony man, standing about five feet nine and a half inches. His features were not regularly handsome, but a remarkably kind and gentle expression amply compensated the defect of mere linear beauty. The fair qualities of his heart shone through his honest face, and I can call to mind no worthier, or, in the active sense of the word, not a more 'good man' than David Harris. He was one of the rare species that link man to man in bonds of fellowship by good works; that inspire confidence, and prevent the structure of society from becoming disjointed, and, 'as it were, a bowing wall, or a tottering fence'. He was a man of so strict a principle, and such high honour, that I believe his moral character was never impeached. I never heard even a suspicion breathed against his integrity, and I knew him long and intimately. I do not mean that he was a *canter*. – Oh, no – no one thought of standing on guard and buttoning up his pockets in Harris's company. I never busied myself about his mode of faith, or the peculiarity of his creed; that was his own affair, not mine, or any other being's on earth; all I know is, that he was an '*honest* man', and the poet has assigned the rank of such a one in creation.

It would be difficult, perhaps impossible, to convey in writing an accurate idea of the grand effect of Harris's bowling; they only who have played against him can fully appreciate it. His attitude when preparing for his run previously to delivering the ball would have made a beautiful study for the sculptor. Phidias would certainly have taken him for a model. First of all, he stood erect like a soldier at drill; then, with a graceful curve of the arm, he raised the ball to his forehead, and drawing back his right foot, started off with his left. The calm look and general air of the man were uncommonly striking, and from this series of preparations he never deviated. I am sure that from this simple account of his manner, all my countrymen who were acquainted with his play will recall him to their minds. His mode of delivering the ball was very singular. He would bring it from under the arm by a twist, and nearly as high as his arm-pit, and with this action *push* it, as it were, from him. How it was the balls acquired the velocity they did by this mode of delivery I never could comprehend.

When he first joined the Hambledon Club, he was quite a raw countryman at cricket, and had very little to recommend him but his noble delivery. He was also very apt to give tosses. I have seen old Nyren scratch his head, and say – 'Harris would make the best bowler in England if he did not toss.' By continual practice, however, and following the advice of the old Hambledon players, he became as steady as could be wished; and in the prime of his playing very rarely indeed gave a toss, although his balls were pitched the full length. In bowling, he never stooped in the least in his delivery, but kept himself upright all the time. His balls were very little beholden to the ground when pitched; it was but a touch, and up again; and woe be to the man who did not get in to block them, for they had such a peculiar curl, that they would grind his fingers against the bat: many a time have I seen the blood drawn in this way from a batter who was not up to the trick; old Tom Walker was the only exception – I have before classed him among the bloodless animals.

Harris's bowling was the finest of all tests for a hitter, and hence the great beauty, as I observed before, of seeing Beldham in, with this man against him; for unless a batter were of the very first class, and accustomed to the best style of stopping, he could do little or nothing with Harris. If the thing had been possible, I should have liked to have seen such a player as Budd (fine hitter as he was) standing against him. My own opinion is that he could not have stopped the balls, and this will be a criterion, by which those who have seen some of that gentleman's brilliant hits may judge of the extraordinary merit of this man's bowling. He was considerably faster than Lambert, and so superior in style and finish that I can draw no comparison between them. Lord Frederick Beauclerk has been heard to say that Harris's bowling was one of the grandest things of the kind he had ever seen; but his lordship could not have known him in his prime; he never saw him play till after he had had many fits of the gout, and had become slow and feeble.

To Harris's fine bowling I attribute the great improvement that was made in hitting, and above all in stopping; for it was utterly impossible to remain at the crease, when the ball was tossed to a fine length; you were obliged to get in, or it would be about your hands, or the handle of your bat; and every player knows where its next place would be.

Some years after Harris had played with the Hambledon Club, he became so well acquainted with the science of the game of cricket that he could take a very great advantage in pitching the wickets. And not only would he pitch a good wicket for himself, but he would also consider those who had to bowl with him. The writer of this has often walked with him up to Windmill-Down at six o'clock in the morning of the day that a match was to be played, and has with pleasure noticed the pains he has taken in choosing the ground for his fellow-bowler as well as himself. The most eminent men in every walk of life have at all times been the most painstaking; – slabberdash work and indifference may accompany genius, and it does so too frequently; such geniuses, however, throw away more than half their chance. There are more brilliant talents in this world than people give the world credit for; and that their lustre does not exhibit to the best advantage, commonly depends upon the owners of them. Ill luck, and the preference that frequently attends industrious mediocrity, are the only anodynes that wounded self-love or indolence can administer to misapplied or unused ability. In his walk, Harris was a man of genius, and he let slip no opportunity to maintain his pre-eminence. Although unwilling to detract from the fame of old Lumpy, I must here observe upon the difference in these two men with regard to pitching their wickets. Lumpy would uniformly select a point where the ball was likely to shoot, that is, over the brow of a little hill; and when by this forethought and contrivance the old man would prove successful in bowling his men out, he would turn round to his party with a little grin of triumph; nothing gratified him like this reward of his knowingness. Lumpy, however, thought only of himself in choosing his ground; his fellow-bowler might take his chance; this was neither wise nor liberal. Harris, on the contrary, as I have already observed, considered his partner; and, in so doing, the main chance of the game. Unlike Lumpy, too, he would choose a rising ground to pitch the ball against, and who is well acquainted with the game of cricket will at once perceive the advantage that must arise from a wicket pitched in this way to such a tremendous bowler as Harris was. If I were urged to draw a comparison between these two great players, the greatest certainly in their department I ever saw, I could do it in no other way than the following: Lumpy's ball was always pitched to the length, but delivered lower than Harris's, and never got up so high; he was also slower than Harris, and lost his advantage by the way in which he persisted in pitching his wicket; yet I think he would bowl more wickets down than the other, for the latter never pitched his wicket with this end in view; almost all his balls, therefore, rose over the wicket; consequently, more players would be caught out from Harris than Lumpy, and not half the number of runs got from his bowling. I passed a very pleasant time with Harris when he came to my father's house at Hambledon, by invitation, after an illness, and for the benefit of the change of air. Being always his companion in his walks about the neighbourhood, I had full opportunity of observing the sweetness of his disposition; this, with his manly contempt of every action that bore the character of meanness, gained him the admiration of every cricketer in Hambledon.

In concluding my recollections of Harris, I had well-nigh omitted to say something of his skill in the other departments of the game. The fact is, the extraordinary merit of his bowling would have thrown any other fair accomplishments he might possess into the shade; but, indeed, as a batter, I considered him rather an indifferent hand; I never recollect his getting more than ten runs, and those very rarely. Neither was his fielding remarkable. But he was game to the backbone, and never suffered a ball to pass him without putting his body in the way of it. If I recollect, he generally played slip.

The Freemantles. There were two of them, and, I believe, brothers. John and Andrew were their names. One was an acknowledged player long before the other began. I am now, however, speaking of Freemantle the bowler. He, with Andrew, came from some town between Winchester and Alresford. John was a stoutly made man; his standard about five feet ten inches. He delivered his ball high and well, and tolerably fast, yet he could not be ranked among the *fast* bowlers. The best compliment I can pay him is that he was reckoned very successful, and, moreover, that his being a member of the Hambledon Club was sufficient guarantee for his general ability, as those sound and experienced judges would never admit as member any man who did not possess some qualifications above the common level.

As a batter, John Freemantle would have been reckoned a good hand in any club. He would now and then get many runs; yet, withal, he could by no means be pronounced a *fine* batter. As a man, he bore a high character for straightforward, manly integrity; in short, he was a hearty John Bull, and flinched no more from doing his duty than he did from a ball in the field, and this he never did, however hard it might hit him.

Andrew was a shortish, well-set man, and a left-handed player. He was an uncommonly safe, as well as good hitter; and few wickets that I could name were more secure than Andrew's. He would often get long hands, and against the best bowling too; and when he had once warmed into his hitting, it was a deuced hard matter to get him out – an accident would frequently do the business. In his general style of batting he very much reminded me of Aylward, who has been spoken of some pages back. He usually played the long field, and was remarkably steady and safe in this department. But Andrew Freemantle could be depended upon, whatever he might undertake, whether in cricket or in his worldly dealings.

Upon one occasion when I had come up to London, I heard of a match being played in Lord's Ground, and of course made one of the spectators of my beloved amusement. Andrew Freemantle was in, and one of the new-fashioned bowlers, commonly called throwers, was bowling to him. His name was Wells, and I believe he came out of Sussex. He was the first I had seen of the new school, after the Walkers had attempted to introduce the system in the Hambledon Club. Wells frequently pitched his balls to the off-side of the wicket to Freemantle's left-handed hitting, who got in before the wicket, and hit the thrower's bowling behind him. Now, had he missed the ball, and it had hit his leg, although before the wicket, he would not have been out, because it had been pitched at the outside of the off-stump. I mention this trifling circumstance to show the knowledge the latter had of the game.

Andrew Freemantle's fielding was very fair; his post was generally the long field. He, however, must be so well known to many of the Mary-le-bone men now living that I need enumerate no more of the peculiar characteristics of his playing.

Next comes that deservedly esteemed character John Small, son, and worthy successor, to the celebrated batter of the same name. He, as well as his father, was a native of Petersfield. Young Small was a very handsomely made man. For perfect symmetry of form, and well-knit, compact limbs and frame, his father was one of the finest models of a man I ever beheld; and the son was little inferior to him in any respect. Jack Small! my old club fellow! when the fresh and lusty May-tide of life sent the blood gambolling through our veins like a Spring runlet, we have had many a good bout together:

'But now my head is bald, John,

And locks as white as snow,' –

and yours have, doubtless, bleached under the cold hand of mayhap three-score winters and more; but the churl has not yet touched the citadel. My heart is as sound as ever, and beats regular and true time to the tune of old and grateful thoughts for long friendships. You, I am sure, can echo this sentiment. You are a musician as well as a friend, and know the value of steadiness in both characters. I think we could give some of the young whipsters a little trouble even now. Like the old Knight of the Boar's Head, we might need the *legs* of these Harry Monmouths; but it is my opinion we could bother them yet, at a good stand to our post. They would find some trouble to bowl down our stumps. They say, Jack, you were born with a bat in your hand. I can believe the tale, for I am sure you inherited the craft from both father and mother. She, I think, took as much delight and interest in the game as he. Many's the time I have seen that worthy woman (every way deserving of so kind and excellent a husband) come galloping up the ground at a grand match, where he was to play (for, you know, she always accompanied him to those high solemnities); and no player even could show more interest in the progress of the game than she, and certainly no one, as was natural, felt so much pride in her husband's fine playing.

I do not remember, John, that you were much of a bowler; but I remember that you were everything else, and that your judgement of the game was equal to that of any man. Your style of hitting, to my mind, was of the very first quality; and I can name no one who possessed a more accurate judgement of a short run. By the by – is the account true which I have heard, that upon one occasion, at Mary-le-bone, you and Hammond went in first, when there were only forty runs to get to win the match; and that you made an agreement together to run whenever the ball passed the wicket-keeper: that you did this, and between you got the whole forty runs before you were out? I have been told this anecdote of you both, and, if true, it clearly shows, according to my opinion, that the judgement of the people who played against you must have been strangely at fault, or they might have prevented it; for had but the long-stop been well acquainted with the game, he would have put you out.

I always admired your fielding, Jack: I am not sure that your middle wicket (the post that your father occupied) was not as good as his – though, I dare say, you would not allow this. Certain am I that a better never was put in that post. And now farewell, my old club-fellow.

Reader! in a few words (now he has left the room), I assure you that in every way he was as complete a chap as I ever knew – a genuine chip off the old block – an admirable player, and a highly honourable man. The legs at Mary-le-bone never produced the least change in him; but, on the contrary, he was thoroughly disgusted at some of the manoeuvres that took place there from time to time.

About the time that John Small had risen into the celebrity I have just been describing, his father and Nyren retired from the field. I cannot do better, in concluding these brief recollections, than enumerate the most eminent players in the Hambledon Club when it was in its glory.

David Harris,	Tom Walker,
John Wells,	——Robinson,
——Purchase,	Noah Mann,
William Beldham	———Scott,
John Small, Jun.	———Taylor,

Harry Walker.

No eleven in England could have had any chance with these men; and I think they might have beaten any two-and-twenty.

From JERKS IN FROM SHORT LEG

BY R. A. FITZGERALD (1866)

SHORT LEG. THIS PLACE SHOULD BE FILLED BY A CHEERFUL MAN. His responsibilities are not so great as those of any other situation; he should be ready with a cheerful remark, and so generally to keep the game alive. In other words. Put your comic man here.

He must be always ready to back up. Don't let him talk to the umpire; but don't let him shrink from knocking that individual down should it be necessary to do so in order to make a catch. Short leg should be careful how he throws; he should have no private animosity or misunderstanding with the wicket-keeper, for he is in a position to inflict upon that gentleman grievous bodily harm.

He should be a man of observation, for no two men play the same at a leg-ball; and he should be ready even to anticipate any wish of the bowler, by watching the batsman's play on the leg side, as many a run is saved by paying attention to the first few overs to each batsman.

Wicket-keeper. Have you got one? Yes – then you are in luck. No – then what are you to do? We confess it is a difficult question to answer. Perhaps the best course is to consult the field generally whether they, or any of their relations, ever filled the situation. Talent sometimes is hereditary. We remember a case where

a gentleman was desired to fill the post, from his stating that he had once heard his father say that he had put the gloves on, but he wasn't sure whether it was in the cricket-field or the P.R. [prize ring]. Many men have risen to eminence with no better recommendation than this. We are inclined to think that, except with slow bowling – where even an apology is better than none – the wickets had better not be kept at all. Your flashy and funky keeper is a terrible worry to the long stop and slips. It is impossible to estimate too highly the qualities that make up a good wicket-keeper. It demands the quickest of eye, the staunchest of nerve, the steadiest of purpose, the most unflinching of resolution. But to the eye and nerve that makes the post pre-eminent, must be added the judgement and art of directing, that will keep all the other posts alive to their work.

The hand, not the voice, must be ready to signify the change required by the batsman's play, and as from his position he is the best judge, so should he be the first to recommend any change in the bowling; strictly speaking, he is the only man in the field entitled to make a remark at all. If he is not, he should be the captain. He should endeavour to inculcate a good style of throwing in, but he should not be above taking a half-volley or a one-hander high to the right or left. As he for the most part tries, and gets his finger ends repeatedly warmed in so trying, more allowance should be made for him than for any other man; and as we have hinted above, an unnecessary hard throw at him is wanton cruelty.

The Plodding Cricketer. To our mind this type is the most painful and most mysterious of all. He plays in more matches than all the other types collected. His name is always found in the penultimate order of going in. He is very seldom a bowler, and is at best a long stop. Yet he hammers on, like the fabulous horse, on the 'ard 'ard road to honour and glory. He is the best-tempered fellow in the world, and his name appears weekly in some facetious contribution to the sporting prints, under some new *nom de guerre*. You may catch him any afternoon at practice; and when he isn't oiling his bat, he is reading Lillywhite's *Guide and Advice to Cricketers*.

Now, in *what* lies the secret of his attachment to the game? Can it be a thirst for success? Surely such a prospect can be but a mirage. Cricket has much of the will-o'-the-wisp delusion about it; it holds out to the plodding cricketer a sufficient glimmer of momentary success to light him on his path; it has so many funny turns and slices of luck, that the most erratic must sometimes fall into the right groove, and the most hungry come in for an unexpected innings at its board.

The Plodder is after all a very useful man in the field. He will always field out when you are a man 'short' (and when are you *not*?) and will, if properly appealed to, for the sake of cricket, go so far as to carry your bag to the railway station; and we hope cricket will never be without many representatives of this little appreciated but valuable type.

From THE FIXED PERIOD

BY ANTHONY TROLLOPE (1882)

Anthony Trollope (1815–1882) needs little introduction, being one of the great English novelists of the nineteenth century. Best known for his Chronicles of Barsetshire – a series of six novels set in the fictional town of Barchester – the tone of the the following story is far more offbeat, being a futuristic account of a game of cricket set in 1980.

* * *

THE DAY FOR THE MATCH HAD COME. IT WAS ALL ENGLAND against Britannula! The two captains tossed for the first innings, and the English club won it. Think of the population of the two countries. We had, however, been taught to believe that no community ever played cricket as did the Britannulans. The English went in first, with two baronets, Sir Kennington and Sir Lords, at the wickets. They looked like two stout Minervas with huge wicker helmets. I know a picture of the goddess, all helmet, spear and petticoats, carrying her spear over her shoulder as she flies through the air over the cities of the earth. Sir Kennington did not fly, but in other respects he was very like the goddess, so completely enveloped was he in his india-rubber guards, and so wonderful was the machine upon his head, by which his brain and features were to be protected.

As he took his place upon the ground there was great cheering. Then the steam-bowler was ridden into its place by the attendant engineer, and Jack began his work. I could see the colour come and go in his face as he carefully placed the ball and peeped down to get its bearing. It seemed to me as though he were taking infinite care to level it straight and even at Sir Kennington's head. I was told afterwards that he never looked at Sir Kennington, but that, having calculated his distance by means of a quicksilver levelling-glass, his object was to throw the ball on a certain inch of turf, from which it might shoot into the wicket at such a degree as to make it very difficult for Sir Kennington to know what to do with it. It seemed to me to take a long time, during which the fourteen men around all looked as though each man were intending to hop off to some other spot than that on which he was standing. There used, I am told, to be only eleven of these men; but, in a great match, the long-offs, and the long-ons, and the rest of them, are all doubled. The double long-off was at such a distance that, he being a small man, I could only just see him through the field-glass which I kept in my waistcoat pocket. When I had been looking hard at them for what seemed to be a quarter of an hour, and the men were apparently becoming tired of their continual hop, and when Jack had stooped and kneeled and sprawled, with one eye shut, in every conceivable attitude, on a sudden there came a sharp snap, a little smoke, and lo, Sir Kennington Oval was . . . out!

There was no doubt about it. I myself saw the two bails fly away into infinite space, and at once there was a sound of kettledrums, trumpets, fifes and clarionets. It seemed as though all the loud music of the town band had struck up at the moment with their shrillest notes. And a huge gun was let off.

> 'And let the kettle to the trumpet speak,
> The trumpet to the cannoneer without,
> The cannons to the heavens, the heavens to earth.
> Now drinks the king to Hamlet.'

I could not but fancy, at these great signs of success, that I was Hamlet's father.

Sir Kennington Oval was out – out at the very first ball. There could be no doubt about it, and Jack's triumph was complete. It was melancholy to see the English Minerva, as he again shouldered his spear and walked back to his tent. In spite of Jack's good play, and the success on the part of my own countrymen, I could not but be sorry to think that the young baronet had come half round the world to be put out at the first ball. There was a cruelty in it, – an inhospitality, – which, in spite of the exigencies of the game, went against the grain. Then, when the shouting, and the hollowing, and the flinging up of the ball were still going on, I remembered that, after it, he would have his consolation with Eva. And poor Jack, when his short triumph was over, would have to reflect that, though fortunate in his cricket, he was unhappy in his love. As this occurred to me, I looked back towards the house, and there, from a little lattice window at the end of the verandah, I saw a lady's handkerchief waving. Could it be that Eva was waving it so as to comfort her vanquished British lover? In the meantime Minerva went to his tent, and hid himself among sympathetic friends; and I was told afterwards that he was allowed half a pint of bitter beer by Dr MacNuffery.

After twenty minutes spent in what seemed to me the very ostentation of success, another man was got to the wickets. This was Stumps, one of the professionals, who was not quite so much like a Minerva, though he, too, was prodigiously greaved. Jack again set his ball, snap went the machine, and Stumps wriggled his bat. He touched the ball, and away it flew behind the wicket. Five republican Minervas ran after it as fast as their legs could carry them; and I was told by a gentleman who sat next to me scoring, that a dozen runs had been made. He spent a great deal of time in explaining how, in the old times, more than six at a time were never scored. Now all this was altered. A slight tip counted ever so much more than a good forward blow, because the ball went behind the wicket. Up flew on all sides of the ground figures to show that Stumps had made a dozen, and two British clarionets were blown with a great deal of vigour. Stumps was a thick-set, solid, solemn-looking man, who had been ridiculed by our side as being much too old for the game; but he seemed to think very little of Jack's precise machine. He kept chopping the ball, which always went behind, till he had made a great score. It was two hours before Jack had sorely lamed him in the hip, and the umpire had given it leg-before-wicket. Indeed it was leg-before-wicket, as the poor man felt when he was assisted back to his tent. However, he had scored 150. Sir Lords Longstop, too, had run up a good score before he was caught out by the middle long-off – a marvellous catch they all said it was – and our trumpets were blown for fully five minutes. But the big gun was only fired when a ball was hurled from the machine directly at the wicket.

At the end of three days the Britishers were all out, and the runs were numbered in four figures. I had my doubts, as I looked at the contest, whether any of them would be left to play out the match. I was informed that I was expected to take the President's seat every day; but when I heard that there were to be two innings for each set, I positively declined. But Crasweller took my place; and I was told that a gleam of joy shot across his worn, sorrowful face when Sir Kennington began the second innings with ten runs. Could he really wish, in his condition, to send his daughter away to England simply that she might be a baronet's wife?

When the Britannulists went in for the second time, they had 1,500 runs to get; and it was said afterwards that Grundle had bet four to one against his own side. This was thought to be very shabby on his part, though if such was the betting, I don't see why he should lose his money by backing his friends. Jack declared in my hearing that he would not put a shilling on. He did not wish either to lose his money or to bet against himself. But he was considerably disheartened when he told me that he was not going in on the first day of the second innings. He had not done much when the Britannulists were in before – had only made some thirty or forty runs; and, worse than that, Sir Kennington Oval had scored up to 300. They told me that his Pallas helmet was shaken with tremendous energy as he made his running. And again, that man Stumps had seemed to be invincible, though still lame, and

had carried out his bat with a tremendous score. He trudged away
without any sign of triumph; but Jack said that the professional
was the best man they had.

On the second day of our party's second innings – the last day
but one of the match – Jack went in. They had only made 150 runs
on the previous day, and three wickets were down. Our
kettledrums had had but little opportunity for making themselves
heard. Jack was very despondent, and had had some tiff with Eva.
He had asked Eva whether she were not going to England, and Eva
had said that perhaps she might do so if some Britannulists did not
do their duty. Jack had chosen to take this as a bit of genuine
impertinence, and had been very sore about it. Stumps was
bowling from the British catapult, and very nearly gave Jack his
quietus during the first over. He hit wildly, and four balls passed
him without touching his wicket. Then came his turn again, and he
caught the first ball with his Neverbend spring-bat – for he had
invented it himself – such a swipe, as he called it, that nobody has
ever yet been able to find the ball. The story goes that it went right
up to the verandah, and that Eva picked it up, and has treasured it
ever since.

Be that as it may, during the whole of that day, and the next,
nobody was able to get him out. There was a continual banging of
the kettledrum which seemed to give him renewed spirits. Every
ball as it came to him was sent away into infinite space. All the
Englishmen were made to retire to further distances from the
wickets, and to stand about almost at the extremity of the ground.
The management of the catapults was entrusted to one man after
another – but in vain. Then they sent the catapults away, and tried
the old-fashioned slow bowling. It was all the same to Jack. He
would not be tempted out of his ground, but stood there awaiting
the ball, let it come ever so slowly. Through the first of the two
days he stood before his wicket, hitting to the right and the left, till
hope seemed to spring up again in the bosom of the Britannulists.
And I could see that the Englishmen were becoming nervous and

uneasy, although the odds were still much in their favour.

At the end of the first day Jack had scored above 500 – but eleven wickets had gone down, and only three of the most inferior players were left to stand up with him. It was considered that Jack must still make another 500 before the game would be won. This would allow only twenty each to the other three players. 'But,' said Eva to me that evening, 'they'll never get the twenty each.'

'And on which side are you, Eva?' I inquired with a smile. For in truth I did believe at that moment that she was engaged to the baronet.

'How dare you ask, Mr Neverbend?' she demanded, with indignation. 'Am not I a Britannulist as well as you?' And as she walked away I could see that there was a tear in her eye.

On the last day feelings were carried to a pitch which was more befitting the last battle of a great war – some Waterloo of other ages – than the finishing of a prolonged game of cricket. Men looked, and moved, and talked as though their all were at stake. I cannot say that the Englishmen seemed to hate us, or we them; but that the affair was too serious to admit of playful words between the parties. And those unfortunates who had to stand up with Jack were so afraid of themselves that they were like young country orators about to make their first speeches. Jack was silent, determined, and yet inwardly proud of himself, feeling that the whole future success of the republic was on his shoulders. He ordered himself to be called at a certain hour, and the assistants in our household listened to his words as though feeling that everything depended on their obedience. He would not go out on his bicycle, as fearing that some accident might occur. 'Although, ought I not to wish that I might be struck dead?' he said; 'as then all the world would know that, though beaten, it had been by the hand of God, and not by our default.' It astonished me to find that the boy was quite as eager about his cricket as I was about my Fixed Period.

At eleven o'clock I was in my seat, and on looking round, I

could see that all the rank and fashion of Britannula were at the ground. But all the rank and fashion were there for nothing, unless they had come armed with glasses. The spaces required by the cricketers were so enormous that otherwise they could not see anything of the play. Under my canopy there was room for five, of which I was supposed to be able to fill the middle thrones. On the two others sat those who officially scored the game. One seat had been demanded for Mrs Neverbend. 'I will see his fate – whether it be his glory or his fall,' said his mother, with true Roman feeling. For the other Eva had asked, and of course it had been awarded to her. When the play began, Sir Kennington was at the catapult and Jack at the opposite wicket, and I could hardly say for which she felt the extreme interest which she certainly did exhibit. I, as the day went on, found myself worked up to such excitement that I could hardly keep my hat on my head or behave myself with becoming presidential dignity. At one period, as I shall have to tell, I altogether disgraced myself.

There seemed to be an opinion that Jack would either show himself at once unequal to the occasion, and immediately be put out – which opinion I think that all Gladstonopolis was inclined to hold – or else that he would get his 'eye in' as he called it, and go on as long as the three others could keep their bats. I know that his own opinion was the same as that general in the city, and I feared that his very caution at the outset would be detrimental to him. The great object on our side was that Jack should, as nearly as possible, be always opposite to the bowler. He was to take the four first balls, making but one run off the last, and then beginning another over at the opposite end do the same thing again. It was impossible to manage this exactly; but something might be done towards effecting it. There were the three men with whom to work during the day. The first unfortunately was soon made to retire; but Jack, who had walked up to my chair during the time allowed for fetching down the next man, told me that he had 'got his eye', and I could see a settled look of fixed purpose in his face. He bowed most gracefully to Eva, who was so stirred by emotion that she could not allow herself to speak a word. 'Oh Jack, I pray for you; I pray for you,' said his mother. Jack, I fancy, thought more of Eva's silence than of his mother's prayer.

Jack went back to his place, and hit the first ball with such energy that he drove it into the other stumps and smashed them to pieces. Everybody declared that such a thing had never been before achieved at cricket – and the ball passed on, and eight or ten runs were scored. After that Jack seemed to be mad with cricketing power. He took off his greaves, declaring that they impeded his running, and threw away altogether his helmet. 'Oh, Eva, is he not handsome?' said his mother, in ecstasy, hanging across my chair. Eva sat quite without a sign. It did not become me to say a word, but I did think that he was very handsome – and I thought also how uncommonly hard it would be to hold him if he should chance to win the game. Let him make what orations he might against the Fixed Period, all Gladstonopolis would follow him if he won this game of cricket for them.

I cannot pretend to describe all the scenes of that day, nor the growing anxiety of the Englishmen as Jack went on with one hundred after another. He had already scored nearly 1,000 when young Grabbe was caught out. Young Grabbe was very popular, because he was so altogether unlike his partner Grundle. He was a fine frank fellow, and was Jack's great friend. 'I don't mean to say that he can really play cricket,' Jack had said that morning, speaking with great authority; 'but he is the best fellow in the world, and will do exactly what you ask him.' But he was out now; and Jack, with over 200 still to make, declared that he gave up the battle almost as lost.

'Don't say that, Mr Neverbend,' whispered Eva.

'Ah yes; we're gone coons. Even your sympathy cannot bring us round now. If anything could do it that would!'

'In my opinion,' continued Eva, 'Britannula will never be beaten as long as Mr Neverbend is at the wicket.'

'Sir Kennington has been too much for us, I fear,' said Jack, with a forced smile, as he retired.

There was now but the one hope left. Mr Brittlereed remained, but he was all. Mr Brittlereed was a gentleman who had advanced nearer to his Fixed Period than any other of the cricketers. He was nearly thirty-five years of age, and was regarded by them all as quite an old man. He was supposed to know all the rules of the game, and to be rather quick in keeping the wicket. But Jack had declared that morning that he could not hit the ball in a week of Sundays. 'He oughtn't to be here,' Jack had whispered; 'but you know how those things are managed.' I did not know how those things were managed, but I was sorry that he should be there, as Jack did not seem to want him.

Mr Brittlereed now went to his wicket, and was bound to receive the first ball. This he did; made one run, whereas he might have made two, and then had to begin the war over. It certainly seemed as though he had done it on purpose. Jack in his passion broke the handle of his spring-bat, and then had half-a-dozen brought to him in order that he might choose another. 'It was his favourite bat,' said his mother, and buried her face in her handkerchief.

I never understood how it was that Mr Brittlereed lived through that over; but he did live, although he never once touched the ball. Then it came to be Jack's turn; and he at once scored thirty-nine during the over, leaving himself at the proper wicket for recommencing the operation. I think that this gave him new life. It added, at any rate, new fire to every Britannulist on the ground, and I must say that after that Mr Brittlereed managed the matter altogether to Jack's satisfaction. Over after over Jack went on, and received every ball that was bowled. They tried their catapult with single, double, and even treble action. Sir Kennington did his best, flinging the ball with his most tremendous impetus, and then just rolling it up with what seemed to me the most provoking languor. It was all the same to Jack. He had in truth got his 'eye in', and as surely as the ball came to him, it was sent away to some most distant part of the ground.

The Britishers were mad with dismay as Jack worked his way on through the last hundred. It was piteous to see the exertions which poor Mr Brittlereed made in running backwards and forwards across the ground. They tried, I think, to bustle him by the rapid succession of their bowling. But the only result was the ball was sent still further off when it reached Jack's wicket. At last, just as every clock upon the ground struck six with that wonderful unanimity which our clocks have attained since they were all regulated by wires from Greenwich, Jack sent a ball flying up into the air, perfectly regardless whether it might be caught or not, knowing well that the one now needed would be scored before it could come down from the heavens into the hands of any Englishman. It did come down, and was caught by Stumps, but by that time Britannula had won her victory. Jack's total score during that innings was 1,275. I doubt whether in the annals of cricket any record is made of a better innings than that. Then it was that, with an absence of that presence of mind which the President of a republic should always remember, I took off my hat and flung it into the air.

Jack's triumph would have been complete, only that it was ludicrous to those who could not but think, as I did, of the very little matter as to which the contest had been raised – just a game of cricket which two sets of boys had been playing, and which should have been regarded as no more than an amusement – as a pastime, by which to refresh themselves between their work. But they regarded it as though a great national combat had been fought, and the Britannulists looked upon themselves as though they had been victorious against England. It was absurd to see Jack as he was carried back to Gladstonopolis as the hero of the occasion, and to hear him, as he made his speeches at the dinner which was given on the day, and at which he was called upon to take the chair. I was glad to see, however, that he was not quite so glib with his tongue as he had been when addressing the people. He hesitated a good deal, nay, almost broke down, when he gave the health of Sir Kennington Oval and the British sixteen; and I was quite pleased to hear Lord Marylebone declare to his mother that he was 'a wonderfully nice boy'. I think the English did try to turn it off a little, as though they had only come out there just for the amusement of the voyage. But Grundle, who had now become quite proud of his country, and who lamented loudly that he should have received so severe an injury in preparing for the game, would not let this pass.

'My lord,' he said, 'what is your population?' Lord Marylebone named sixty million.

'We are but two hundred and fifty thousand,' said Grundle, 'and see what we have done.'

'We are cocks fighting on our own dunghill,' said Jack, 'and that does make a deal of difference.'

But I was told that Jack had spoken a word to Eva in quite a different spirit before he had left Little Christchurch. 'After all, Eva, Sir Kennington has not quite trampled us under his feet,' he said.

'Who thought that he would?' said Eva. 'My heart has never fainted, whatever some others may have done.'

BAXTER'S SECOND INNINGS

ANONYMOUS (1892)

'LIFE IS SIMPLY A CRICKET MATCH – WITH TEMPTATION AS BOWLER.
He's the fellow who takes nearly every boy's wicket some
time or other. But perhaps you can't stand this, Baxter. I'll stop it.'
'No,' said Baxter, 'I'm as right as a trivet. Please go on. I know you
won't preach.'
'Well,' continued the Captain, 'stop me if I bore you. You see
every boy has three wickets to defend. The first is Truth, the
second Honour, the third Purity.'

From CREATURES OF CIRCUMSTANCES

BY HORACE HUTCHINSON (1891)

Horace Hutchinson (1859–1932) was not only a great all-round
sportsman but he also wrote the first cricketing novel, *Peter Steele,
The Cricketer*, which was published in 1896, as well as compiling
the first cricket anthology, *Cricket Saws and Stories*.

* * *

OF LATTER YEARS THE CRICKET IN THE ANNUAL MATCH, LITTLE
Pipkin against White-Cross, had not been going at all as Mr
Slocombe could have wished. It was not merely that Little Pipkin
had been beaten, but a custom had crept in of asking foreign
cricketers – men not in the county even – to take part in the match.
The innovation had been commenced by White-Cross, and Mr
Slocombe was liberal enough to admit that White-Cross had had

some reason for the step – in fact, that it was rendered necessary, if the match were to be a match at all, by the over-mastering genius of Robert Burscough. So far he even approved of it as a just recognition on the part of White-Cross of Little Pipkin's superiority.

But now Robert was gone. This was the third year that he had been unable to come to the match, for the year before he went abroad an even greater fixture had hindered him, and by the help of foreign allies – men whose names were of note even at Lord's – White-Cross had given Little Pipkin two parlous beatings. This year Colonel Burscough, on the part of Little Pipkin, had written to Lord Morningham as representing White-Cross, proposing, as Robert was abroad, that they should return to the good old ways, and that the match should again become one of village teams pure and simple. But Lord Morningham could not agree to this, because, as he said, his guests were already invited. So Colonel Burscough devised a scheme almost Cheadleian in its subtlety, and laid it before the cricket committee of Little Pipkin, in whose eyes it found favour, and they were all sworn to secrecy respecting it.

On the day of the great match Lord Morningham drove over in his dogcart with two of his friends, betimes, and another friend, and the rest of the eleven of White-Cross, in a drag, were not long behind him. When they came out of the dressing-tent the eleven of White-Cross presented a splendour that charmed the eye with the colours of the I. Zingari, Free Foresters, and M.C.C. adorning the persons of the three imported cricketers; while the appearance of the eleven of Little Pipkin was of pure, unrelieved rusticity. But some of the men of White-Cross began to ask one another who was that rustic with the long legs and the hat pulled over his eyes; and who that one with the stout legs? There was also a third who was a stranger to them, but he escaped general notice because he was of little stature. They asked the men of Little Pipkin who these men were, and some said, quite truly, that they did not know, and others that the strangers had but lately come to the village; and this

again was true, for they had
come to it but the night before.

White-Cross won the toss, and Lord Morningham sat in the
pavilion and watched the first of his friends, who was a mighty
swiper, go in, and settled himself to see him swipe. The long-legged
stranger rustic began to bowl. At the first ball Lord Morningham
whistled after a manner he had when in the pavilion at Lord's; for
he affected cricket, as being a popular game, and because he had
been the coolest slow bowler for an Eton boy that had ever
trundled out a Harrow eleven. But he whistled because the ball
went so fearfully near the wicket. To the second ball the batsman
played forward carefully, and met it. But the third pitched a trifle
shorter, and the batsman, playing forward as before, returned it to
the hands of the bowler, where it remained.

The most terrible catastrophes are those that happen most
suddenly, and in quick succession the wickets fell of the other two
whose names were great at Lord's, and they were together in the
pavilion explaining to each other the causes of their several
downfalls, which they agreed in attributing to luck, and expressed
every confidence that, given another trial, they could go on playing
that sort of bowling all day long. For the other bowler was the
stranger rustic who had escaped notice by his shortness of stature.

Disheartened by the defeat of their best and brightest, the eleven of White-Cross were all out for twenty-seven, and byes had contributed the most of these.

Then it was the turn of Little Pipkin to go in, and the short stranger rustic and the stout-legged stranger rustic went to the wickets. And despite all the efforts of the friends of Lord Morningham, whose names were so great at Lord's, they were at the wickets still when the luncheon bell rang; and most of this time had been spent by the eleven of White-Cross, assisted by the entire village of Little Pipkin, in hunting for the ball in the hedge of the vicarage glebe, into which these stranger rustics repeatedly hit it. And the telegraph read 137, and that only, for of wickets fallen there was no tale to tell. At the beginning of luncheon the strangers were conspicuous by their absence, but after a short time they came in, no longer in their rustic garb, but in the unclouded majesty of white flannel. And Lord Morningham and his friends at once recognized them, and gave a shout, for the long rustic was a very famous bowler of the Surrey eleven, and the stout-legged rustic was the best batsman on a mud-wicket in all England (the champion not excepted), and the rustic of short stature was the most brilliant fieldsman of the eleven of Lancashire, and good with bat and ball alike.

Thus Colonel Burscough schemed Cheadleianly, and accomplished the overthrow of the men of White-Cross and their famous allies; and when they saw by whom they had been defeated they felt no shame and bore no malice, but joined in the laugh against themselves.

INTRODUCTION TO
RICHARD DAFT'S *KINGS OF CRICKET*

BY ANDREW LANG (1893)

Andrew Lang (1844–1912) is probably best remembered for his collections of fairy tales (each one being named after a different colour). He also wrote many history books – among others *The Mystery of Mary Stuart* (1901), *James VI and the Gowrie Conspiracy* (1902) and *John Knox and the Reformation* (1905). The following piece introduces Richard Daft's (1835–1900) book *Kings of Cricket*. Daft himself played regularly for the county of Nottinghamshire for twenty-two years, becoming captain in 1872. He was described by Horace Hutchinson as 'the model of a correct, sound, and graceful style of batting'.

* * *

M R DAFT HAS REQUESTED ME TO WRITE AN INTRODUCTION TO the volume of his *Kings of Cricket*. It is an old saying that 'Good wine needs no bush', and I scarcely see how the remarks of one who is living disproof of a maxim of Mr Daft's can help the cause of the game. 'Anyone ought to make himself into a fair player by perseverance,' observed this authority. Alas! long and bitter experience has taught me that there was one exception, at least, to a rule which observation convinces me is far from general. A cricketer is born, not made. A good eye and stout muscles are necessary: and though Mr Daft thinks highly of the intellectual element in cricket, it remains true that 'muscles make the man, not mind, nor that confounded intellect'.

As to intellect, it is not so very hard to invent 'head-balls'. After weeks of reflection, I once invented a 'head-ball' myself.

First, you send your man a ball tossed rather high, but really pitched rather short. The batsman detects this, or if he does not and goes in to drive it, so much the better. If he does detect it, you follow it up by a ball really pitched up, but of the same height in curve as the former. The batsman plays back again, thinking it is the same ball, and usually makes a mistake. Such studies in the subjectivity of the batsman are easily elaborated in the closet, but when it comes to practice he usually hits across the hop of the first ball and drives the second over the pavilion. In consequence of these failures to make the means attain the end, I have never taken part in really first-class cricket – not beyond playing once for my college eleven. But one beauty of cricket is that, if you cannot play at it, you can at least look on and talk very learnedly, and find fault with the captain, showing how you would order matters if you were consulted. This is the recreation of middle age, and is permitted to an incapacity for actual performance which the audience never heard of or have had time to forget.

About Mr Daft's own play it is not possible, were it desirable, for me to offer criticism, as I never saw him save on one occasion. I had gone to Nottingham to view Gloucestershire play Notts, as two Clifton boys, friends of mine, were playing for the western county. One of them was bowling, and it is not ungracious to say that he was far from being a colossus. As Mr Daft came in, one of the crowd observed: 'I would like to see the little 'un bowl Daft!' which surely was a chivalrous expression of an Englishman's preference for the weaker side. However, the prayer was scattered to the winds. The ball, too, visited the boundaries of the Trent Bridge ground, and Notts made over five hundred.

Though one did not see very much first-class cricket before 1874, the memories of what one has seen and read about abide among our most pleasant reminiscences. Cricket is among the few institutions in England which Time has not spoiled, nay, has rather improved. The wickets are better, immeasurably better than of old. The bowling is better, the fielding is as good as ever; probably the wicket-keeping is improved, and the general temper of players and spectators leaves nothing to be desired. A fine day at the Oval makes us all akin, and a pleasant sight it is to see the vast assembly, every man with his eyes riveted on the wicket, every man able to appreciate the most delicate strokes in the game, and anxious to applaud friend or adversary. An English cricketing crowd is as fair and as generous as any assembly of mortals may be. When the Australians defeat us, though we do not like it, we applaud them till these bronzed Colonists almost blush. It is not so in all countries, nor in all countries is there the ready acceptance of the umpire's verdict, without which cricket degenerates into a wrangle.

Mr Daft is not inclined to believe that the veterans of a middle-aged man's youth were inferior to the heroes of our later day. With Dr W. G. Grace, indeed, no man competes or has competed. The hardness and subtlety of his hitting and placing of the ball, his reach and certainty at such a field as point, and the sagacious perseverance which he displays as a bowler, combine to make him unique: 'W. G.' – a name to resound for ages.

There is something monumental in his stance at the wicket, wholly free from a false refinement, without extraneous elegancies. His is a nervous, sinewy, English style, like that of Fielding. Better graced cricketers we may have seen, such as Mr Edward Lyttelton, Mr Charles Studd, Mr A. G. Steel, all of them, in their day, models of classical dexterity and refinement. But it is always, or almost always, Dr W. G. Grace's day: his play is unhasting, unresting, like the action of some great natural law. With him, then, nobody can compare; and we who have seen

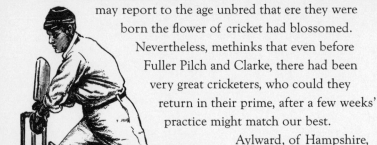

may report to the age unbred that ere they were born the flower of cricket had blossomed. Nevertheless, methinks that even before Fuller Pilch and Clarke, there had been very great cricketers, who could they return in their prime, after a few weeks' practice might match our best.

Aylward, of Hampshire, must have been a truly sterling batsman.

Lambert may also be reckoned among the immortals, and it is highly probable that David Harris, on those wickets which he knew how to prepare, would puzzle even men like Shrewsbury.

In those days the bowler laid out his wicket to suit himself. None of us now living can equal the old underhand bowling, which, in some mysterious way, was delivered high, from under the armpit, got up very fast and erect from the pitch, and was capable of many changes of curve and pitch. Brown, of Brighton, and others, appear to have bowled underhand as fast, or faster, than Tarrant, or Jackson, or Mr Cecil Boyle. This seems quite probable. Perhaps the swiftest bowling I ever saw was the underhand of a fast roundhand bowler, now in Canada, and at no time known to fame. He is a clergyman of the Scottish church, the 'Jointer', so styled of yore. 'He says he's a meenister, he says he's a beginner; I think he's a leear,' observed the caddie, when asked, at golf, who this gentleman might be. Hail, Jointer, across the wide seas and the many years, I salute thee. *Bayete!* as the Zulu says.

Now, allowing for odd wickets, and for the peculiarities of very fast underhand with a high delivery, it seems likely, that on an old Hampshire wicket, Nyren's team might have tackled as good an eleven as we moderns could send to meet them. In the fields of asphodel (which, of course, would need returfing), some such game may be played by heroes dead and gone.

But in this world one can never thus measure strength any more than we can judge of old actors, and compare Molière to Garrick, and Garrick to Monsieur Poquelin. The cricketer, unlike the actor, leaves something permanent – his scores; but we cannot discover the true equation, as the different conditions cannot be estimated. Thus in golf, a round of 94, on St Andrews Links, in 1761, with feathered balls, and unkempt putting greens, and whins all over the links, is surely at least as good as Hugh Kirkcaldy's round of 73 today, now that the iron age has come in, and the baffy spoon exists only as a venerable relic. Men's thews and skill have ever been much on a level.

It is the conditions that alter, and all old cricketers will believe in the old heroes of the past. To do so is pleasant, pious, and provides a creed not to be shaken by criticism. We who remember Carpenter and Hayward, Caffyn and H. H. Stephenson, are not to be divorced from the idols. They wore 'billy-cock' hats (the true word is bully-cock) and oddly-coloured shirts, and blue belts with snake clasps, and collars and neckties, as their great-grandfathers had worn jockey caps and knee-breeches, and their fathers tall hats. But these were unessential details.

The style in bowling of that age – Caffyn's age – with level arm, was peculiarly graceful. The command of the ball was less than at present. Peate's delivery was level, or nearly level; yet his dexterity was unsurpassed. The most favourable admirers can hardly call Mr Spofforth's style a model of grace. It has withal a something truculent and overbearing. Yet, on the modern wickets, bowling needs every fair advantage that it can obtain, and throwing has gone distinctly out of favour. I remember an excellent cricketer and most successful bowler, concerning whom I chanced to remark to a friend that I thought him quite fair. 'I think him a capital man to have on our side', was the furthest to which my companion's lenity of judgement would stretch. Probably no bowler throws consciously, but it was certainly high time that umpires should bring some fast bowlers to the test of an objective standard.

When roundhand bowling came in, the veteran Nyren declared that all was over with the game; that it would become a mere struggle of physical force. But, for this once, pessimism was mistaken, and prophecy unfulfilled. Still there was the grace of a day that is dead in the old level deliveries, while some slinging bowlers, of whom Mr Powys, I think, was the last, could be extremely dangerous, if occasionally erratic. The regrets of him who praises times past are natural, but are tempered.

As for the present day, we are all tired – Mr Daft is tired – of the Fabian policy which leaves balls to the off alone, in a scientific cowardice. Once Mr Ernest Steel, then by no means a big boy, playing for Marlborough, at Lord's, taught a Rugby boy the unwisdom of this course. He bowled two balls to the off which were left alone; the third looked like them, but broke viciously, was left alone, and down went the off stump. This was not in first-class

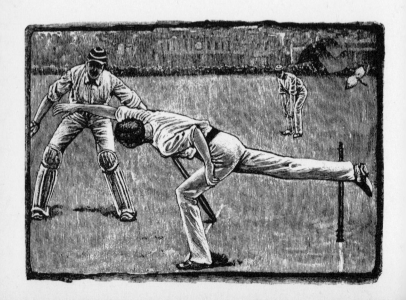

cricket, but it was a pleasant thing to see and remember. Many such pleasant memories recur to an old spectator.

There was Ulyett's catch, at Lord's, when the gigantic Mr Bonnor drove a ball to the off, invisible for its speed, and the public looked to see where the ring would divide. But the ball was in Ulyett's hands. There was Mr A. J. Webbe's catch of Mr Edward Lyttelton, who had hit a ball, low and swift as a half-topped golf ball, to the ropes. Running along the ropes, Mr Webbe caught it, low down, at full speed, a beautiful exhibition of graceful activity. Pindar would have commemorated it in an ode, and Dioscorides in a gem. Mr G. F. Grace's catch, under the pavilion at the Oval, I had not the fortune to witness, but Mr Gale has described it in impassioned prose. Then there was Mr Steel's bowling, in his youthful prime, a sad sight for Oxford eyes, when the ball seemed alive and unplayable. Mr Berkeley's bowling at Lord's, in 1891, at the end of the second Cambridge innings, was also a thing to dream upon, when for a moment it seemed as if the glories of Mr Cobden were to be repeated; but Mr Woods was there! As to Mr V. T. Hill's innings, in 1892, I cannot speak of it in prose.

Mr Daft has not dwelt much on University cricket, the most powerfully exciting to the spectator whose heart is in the right place (not unfrequently 'in his mouth') when we wait for a catch to come to hand. The memories of old players in these affairs – Mr Mitchell, Mr Ottaway, Mr Yardley, Mr Steel, Mr Kemp (who won matches by sheer pluck and force of character), are fragrant and immortal. There is not talk, when memory sharpens memory, and the dead live again – the regretted, the unforgotten – and the old happy days of burned out Junes revive. We shall not see them again. We lament that lost lightness of heart, 'for no man under the sun lives twice, outliving his day', and the day of the cricketer is brief. It is not every one who can go on playing, 'once you come to forty years', like Mr Daft and Dr W. G. Grace; the eye loses its quickness. An old man at point must be a very courageous old man; the hand loses its cunning, the ball from the veteran fingers has no work nor spin, and the idea of throwing in 'from the country' is painfully distasteful. Dr E. M. Grace, of course, is not old; he reckons not by years. Fortunately, golf exists as a solace of old age, and trout can always be angled for; and to lose a trout is only loss, not 'infinite dishonour' like missing a catch.

Cricket is a very humanizing game. It appeals to the emotions of local patriotism and pride. It is eminently unselfish; the love of it never leaves us, and binds all the brethren together, whatever their politics and rank may be. There is nothing like it in the sports of mankind. Everyone, however young, can try himself at it, though excellence be for the few, or perhaps not entirely for the few. At Nottingham, during the practice hour, how many wonderfully good bowlers you see, throwing off their coats and playing without even cricket shoes. How much good cricket there is in the world!

If a brief and desultory sermon may end with a collection, as is customary, I would fain ask cricketers to remember the London Playing Fields Committee, and send their mites to provide the grounds for those eager young players who draw their wickets with chalk on the wall, or bowl at a piled heap of jackets. Their hearts are in the right place, if their wickets are not, and we can help to get them better grounds. Many good cricketers are on the Committee of the Playing Fields. I believe a cheque to Mr Theodore Hall, Oxford and Cambridge Club, Pall Mall, will go to the right place also. So pay up, that young town-bred boys may play up, ye merry men of England.

Cricket ought to be to English boys what Habeas Corpus is to Englishmen, as Mr Hughes says in *Tom Brown*.

At no ruinous expense, village cricket might also be kept alive and improved; for cricket is a liberal education in itself, and demands temper and justice and perseverance. There is more teaching in the playground than in schoolrooms, and a lesson better worth learning very often. For there can be no good or enjoyable cricket without enthusiasm – without sentiment, one may almost say; a quality that enriches life and refines it; gives it, what life more and more is apt to lose, zest.

Though he who writes was ever a cricketing failure, he must acknowledge that no art has added so much to his pleasures as this English one, and that he has had happier hours at Lord's, or even on a rough country wicket, than at the Louvre or in the Uffizi. If this be true of one, it is probably true of the many whose pleasures are scant, and can seldom come from what is called culture.

Cricket is simply the most catholic and diffused, the most innocently, kindly, and manly of popular pleasures, while it has been the delight of statesmen and the relaxation of learning. There was an old Covenanting minister of the straitest sect, who had so high an opinion of curling that he said if he were to die in the afternoon, he could imagine no better way than curling of passing the morning. Surely we may say as much for cricket. Heaven (as the bishop said of the strawberry) might doubtless have devised a better diversion, but as certainly no better has been invented than that which grew up on the village greens of England.

From PICKWICK PAPERS

BY CHARLES DICKENS (1837)

Charles Dickens (1812–1870) wrote *The Posthumous Papers of the Pickwick Club* for magazine publication (in monthly instalments) at the tender age of twenty-four. In this work Dickens realized his gift for humour and with the book's publication came not only fame, but fortune. The following extract, which describes a match between Dingley Dell and All-Muggleton, is famous in cricketing circles. I never tire of reading it.

* * *

'CAPITAL GAME – WELL PLAYED – SOME STROKES ADMIRABLE,' said the stranger as both sides crowded into a tent, at the conclusion of the game.

'You have played it, Sir?' inquired Mr Wardle, who had been much amused by his loquacity.

'Played it! Think I have – thousands of times – not here – West Indies – exciting thing – hot work – very.'

'It must be rather a warm pursuit in such a climate,' observed Mr Pickwick.

'Warm! – red hot – scorching – glowing. Played a match once – single wicket – friend the Colonel – Sir Thomas Blazo – who should get greatest number of runs. – Won the toss – first innings – seven o'clock, a.m. – six natives to look out – went in; kept in – heat intense – natives all fainted – taken away – fresh half-dozen ordered – fainted also – Blazo bowling – supported by two natives – couldn't bowl me out – fainted too – cleared away the Colonel – wouldn't give in – faithful attendant – Quanko Samba – last man left – sun so hot, bat in blisters, ball scorched brown – five hundred and seventy runs – rather exhausted – Quanko mustered up last remaining strength – bowled me out – had a bath, and went out to dinner.'

'And what became of what's-his-name, Sir?' inquired an old gentleman.

'Blazo?'

'No – the other gentleman.'

'Quanko Samba?'

'Yes, Sir.'

'Poor Quanko – never recovered it – bowled on, on my account – bowled off, on his own – died, Sir.' Here the stranger buried his countenance in a brown jug, but whether to hide his emotion or imbibe its contents, we cannot distinctly affirm. We only know that he paused suddenly, drew a long and deep breath, and looked anxiously on, as two of the principal members of the Dingley Dell club approached Mr Pickwick, and said –

'We are about to partake of a plain dinner at the Blue Lion, Sir; we hope you and your friends will join us.'

'Of course,' said Mr Wardle, 'among our friends we include Mr—;' and he looked towards the stranger.

'Jingle,' said that versatile gentleman, taking the hint at once. 'Jingle – Alfred Jingle, Esq., of No Hall, Nowhere.'

MOCK OBITUARY IN
THE SPORTING TIMES

BY REGINALD SHIRLEY BROOKS (1882)

IN AFFECTIONATE REMEMBRANCE OF ENGLISH CRICKET, WHICH DIED at the Oval, on 29th August, 1882. Deeply lamented by a large circle of sorrowing friends and acquaintances. R.I.P.
N.B. The body will be cremated and the ashes taken to Australia.

VITAÏ LAMPADA

BY SIR HENRY NEWBOLT (1897)

Sir Henry John Newbolt (1862–1938) was a barrister, author and poet, best known for his patriotic and nautical verse. His *Naval History of the War, 1914–1918*, appeared in 1920.

* * *

There's a breathless hush in the Close to-night –
Ten to make and the match to win –
A bumping pitch and a blinding light,
An hour to play and the last man in.
And it's not for the sake of a ribboned coat,
Or the selfish hope of a season's fame,
But his Captain's hand on his shoulder smote –
'Play up! play up! and play the game!'

The sand of the desert is sodden red –

Red with the wreck of a square that broke –
The Gatling's jammed and the Colonel dead,
And the regiment blind with dust and smoke.
The river of death has brimmed his banks,
And England's far and Honour a name,
But the voice of a schoolboy rallies the ranks:
'Play up! play up! and play the game!'

This is the word that year by year,
While in her place the School is set,
Every one of her sons must hear,
And none that hears it dare forget.
This they all with a joyful mind
Bear through life like a torch in flame,
And falling, fling to the host behind –
'Play up! play up! and play the game!'

A BOWLER'S INNINGS

BY E. W. HORNUNG (CIRCA 1900)

E. W. Hornung (1866–1921) was the creator of Raffles, the
Gentleman Cracksman. He married Sir Arthur Conan Doyle's
sister Constance, and although Conan Doyle's Sherlock Holmes is
the more famous character, Raffles runs him a close second. It is
also interesting to note that as George Orwell once said, 'In making
Raffles a cricketer as well as a burglar, Hornung was not merely
providing him with a plausible disguise; he was also drawing the
sharpest moral contrast that he was able to imagine.' The following
short story, though somewhat melancholic, is an example of
Hornung at his best.

* * *

I WAS IN SEARCH OF SOME QUIET SPOT TO WORK IN OVER THE
Christmas holidays, and here under my handlebars was the very
place: a sheltered hollow with a solitary house set close beside the
frozen road. Transversely ran a Yorkshire beck, overfed with snow,
and on the opposite bank the pinched trees rose intricate and
brittle and black against the setting sun. But what pleased me more
was the blue signboard hanging immovable in the windless frost.
And the yellow legend on the same, when I had back-pedalled
down the hill, and was near enough to read it, was to yield the
keenest joy of all:

BLUEBELL INN

Richard Unthank

Dick Unthank! The Old Yorkshire bowler! The most popular
player of his day! It must be the same; the name was uncommon;
and was not inn-keeping the last state of most professional

cricketers? I had never spoken to Unthank in my life; but I had
kept his analysis when a small enthusiast, and had seen him bowl
so often that the red good-humoured face, with crafty hook-nose
and the ginger moustache, was a very present vision as I entered the
inn where I made sure of finding it. A cold deserted passage led me
to a taproom as empty and as cold. No sign of Dick could I
discover; but in the taproom I was joined by a sour-looking slattern
with a grimy baby in her arms.

'Mrs Unthank, I presume?'

'Yes, I'm Mrs Unthank,' said the woman, with a sigh which
offended me. Her voice was as peevish as her face.

'Am I right in taking your husband to be the famous old
cricketer, Dick Unthank?'

'I don't know, I'm sure; he's not that old.'

'But he is the cricketer?'

'Ay; he used to play.'

'Used to play!' I echoed with some warmth. 'Only for the
County, and the Players, and England itself!'

'So I've heard tell,' returned Dick's wife indifferently; 'it was
before my time, you see.'

'Is your husband at home?' cried I, out of patience with the
woman.

'Ay; he's at home!' was the meaning reply.

'Busy?'

'I wish he was! No such luck; he's bad in bed.'

Dick Unthank ill in bed! I thought of that brick-red
countenance and of the arm of gnarled oak which could bowl all
day on a batsman's wicket, and I felt sure it could be nothing
serious. Meanwhile I was looking at the woman, who was either
entirely ignorant or else wilfully unappreciative of her husband's
fame, and I also felt that the least indisposition would become
aggravated in such hands. I said that I should like to see Mr
Unthank, if I might, and if he would see me.

'Are you a friend of his?' inquired the wife.

'I have known him for years – on the cricket-field.'

'Well, t'doctor said coompany was good for him; and dear knows I can't be with him all day, with his work to do as well as my own. If you step this way, I'll show you up. Mind your head as you come upstairs. It's the ricketiest old house iver *I* was in, an' no good for trade an' all; but Mr Unthank took a fancy to it, and he wouldn't listen to me. I doubt he's sorry now. This is the room at t'top o' t'stairs. Oh, no, he won't be asleep. Well, Unthank, here's a gentleman come to see you.'

We entered a square, low room, with no carpet upon its lumpy floor, and very little furniture within its dingy walls. There was one window, whose diamond panes scored the wintry glow across and across, and this was what first caught my eye. Then it rested on the fire in which the coal had been allowed to cake until it gave out as little warmth as light. The bed was in the darkest corner of the room. I could make out little more than a confused mass of bedclothes and, lying back upon the pillows, the head and shoulders of a man.

'He says he's known you for years,' added Mrs Unthank as I shut the door.

'Why, who can it be?' said a hollow voice from the corner. 'Poke up the fire, missus, an' let's see each other.'

'You won't know me, Mr Unthank,' I hastened to confess. 'I have only seen you play, but you have given me many a happy hour, and I wanted to tell you so when I saw your name on the signboard. I am only sorry to find you like this. Nothing very serious, I hope?'

'Not it!' was the hoarse reply. 'It's nobbut a cold I caught last spring, an' never properly throwed off. It serves me right for giving up the game! I'd have sweaten it off in half an hour at the nets. But I mean to give this up, an' get a school or club to coach next season, then I'll be myself again. That's better, missus! Now we can see to shake hands.'

And he gave me the cunning member which had been a

county's strength; but the Dick Unthank of
old days was dead to me before I felt its
slack and humid clasp. The man on the fire-
lit bed seemed half Dick's size, the
lusty arms were gone to skin
and bone, the weather-
beaten face shone whiter
than the unclean pillow which
was its frame. The large nose
was wasted and unduly
prominent, and a red
stubble covered the sunken
cheeks and the chin. Only
the moustache was ruddy
and unchanged; and it
glistened with a baleful dew.
I was utterly amazed and
shocked. How I looked I do not know, but Mrs Unthank paused at
the door before leaving us together.

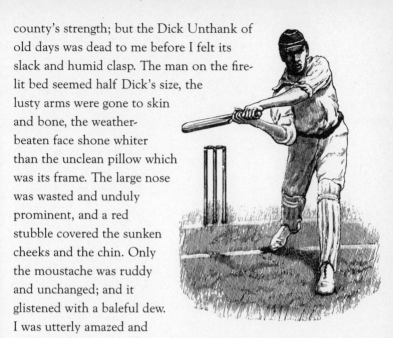

'Ay,' said she, 'I thought you'd see a difference! He talks about
playing next season, but he'll be lucky if he sees another. I doubt
he isn't that long for this world!'

It was my first experience of the class which tells the truth to
its sick and dying, and my blood was boiling; but Unthank smiled
grimly as the door closed.

'Poor lass,' said he, 'it would be hard on her if there was owt in
what she says. But trust a woman to see black, an' trust old Dick to
put on flesh and muscle once he gets back into flannels. I never
should ha' chucked it up; that's where I made a mistake. But spilt
milk's spilt milk, and I'm right glad to see you, sir. So you've
watched me bowl, have you? Not at my best, I'm afraid, sir, unless
you're older than what I take you for.' And Dick looked sorry for
himself for the first time.

'On the contrary,' said I, 'you never did much better than the very first time I saw you play.'

'When was that, sir?'

'Eighteen years ago last July.'

'Eighteen year? Why you must have been a little lad, sir?'

'I was twelve; but I knew my *Lillywhite* off by heart, and all that season I cut the matches out of the newspapers and pasted them in a book. I have it still.'

'Mebbe it wasn't a first-class match you saw me come off in?'

'It was against the Gentlemen, at Lord's.'

'Eighteen – year – ago. Hold on, sir! Did I take some wickets in t'second innings?'

'Seven for forty-three.'

'An' made some runs an' all?'

'Thirty-two not out. It was the fastest thing I ever saw!'

Dick shook his head.

'It wasn't good cricket, sir,' said he. 'But then I never was owt of a bat. It was a bowler's innings was that – a short life but a merry one; it was a bowler's wicket an' all, I mind, an' I was in a hurry to make use of it. Ay, ay, I remember it now as if it were yesterday.'

'So do I; it was my first sight of Lord's.'

'Did you see the ball that took W. G.?'

'I did. It nearly made me cry! It was my first sight of W. G. also!'

'She came back nine inches,' said the old bowler in a solemn voice. 'Mr Grace, he said eighteen inches, and the *Sportsman* it said six; but it wasn't less than nine, as sure as I lie here. Ay, t'wicket might ha' been made for me that day; there's no ground to bowl on like Lord's on the mend. I got Mr Lucas too – and there wasn't a finer batsman living at the time – an' Mr Webbe was caught off me at cover. Them were the days, an' no mistake, an' yon day was one o' my very best; it does me good to think about it. I may never play first-class cricket again, but mebbe I'll coach them as will.'

The fire had died down again; the wintry glow was blotted out

by early night, and once more the old professional's face was invisible in the darkened room. I say 'old' because he had been very long before the public, but he was little worse than forty in mere years, and now in the dark it was difficult to believe that his cricket days were altogether over. His voice was fuller and heartier than when he greeted me, and if the belief that one will recover be half the battle against sickness then Dick Unthank was already half-way to victory. But his gaunt face haunted me, and I was wondering whether such wasted limbs could ever fill out again, when there came a beating of hoofs like drumsticks on the frozen road, and wheels stopped beneath the window.

'That's the doctor,' grumbled Dick. 'I'm sure I don't know what he wants to come every day for. Sit still, sir, sit still.'

'No; I must go. But I shall want something to eat, and a bed for the night at least, and I shall come up later without fail.'

Already there were steps on the rickety stairs; and I made my escape as Mrs Unthank, with a streaming candle, ushered in a tall old gentleman in a greatcoat and creaking boots. I was detaching my impedimenta from the bicycle when the creaking boots came down again.

'I should like one word with you, sir,' said the doctor. 'I gather that you are thinking of putting up here, and it will be a real charity if you do. You have done my patient more good in half an hour than I have in the last month.'

'Oh, as to that,' said I, 'it is a treat to me to meet an old cricketer like Dick Unthank, but I hardly think I can stay beyond to-morrow. I want a quiet place to do some work in, but I must be reasonably comfortable too; and, to be frank, I doubt the comfort here.'

'You may well!' exclaimed the doctor, lowering his voice. 'That woman is enough to scare anybody; yet for the money's sake she would look after you in a way, and with it she might make her husband more comfortable than he is. I may frighten you away myself by saying so, but it would be an untold relief to me to feel that there was one responsible and humane person in the house.'

'Is he so very ill?'

'So very ill? Have you seen him and can you ask? He is in a galloping consumption.'

'But he is so full of hope. Is there no hope for him?'

'Not the shadow of a chance! They are always sanguine. That is part of the disease.'

'And how long do you give him?'

The doctor shrugged. 'It may be weeks, it may be days, it *might* be months,' said he. 'I can only say that in this weather and with such a nurse nothing would surprise me.'

'That is enough for me,' I replied. 'I shall give the place a trial.'

And I did. Many nights I passed in a chamber as accessible to

the four winds of heaven as to the companies of mice which broke
each night's sleep into so many naps. Many days I lived well
enough on new-laid eggs and Yorkshire ham, and wrought at my
book until for good or ill the stack of paper lay complete upon the
table. And many a winter's evening I spent at Dick's bedside,
chatting with him, listening to him, hearing a score of anecdotes to
one that I can set down here, and admiring more and more the
cheeriness and the charity of the dying man. In all our talks I
cannot remember an unkind story or a word of spite, though Dick
had contemporaries still in the county ranks, the thought of whom
must have filled his soul with envy. Even his wife was all that was
good in his eyes; in mine she was not actually bad, but merely
useless, callous and indifferent from sheer want of intelligence and
imagination.

In the early days I sent for my portmanteau, and had my old
cricket scrap-book put into it. Dick's eyes glistened as he took up
leaf after leaf. I had torn them out for his convenience, and for
days they kept him amused while I was absent at my work.
Towards the end I brought my work beside him, for he was
weakening visibly, though unconsciously, and it was a new interest
to his simple mind.

'I don't know how you do it, sir,' said he one afternoon, as I
gathered my papers together. 'I've been watching you this half-hour
– your pen's hardly stopped – and it's all out of your own head! It
beats an' bowls me, sir, does that. Dear knows how you do it.'

'Well,' I laughed, 'and it's a puzzle to me how you pitch a ball
just where you like and make it break either way at will. Dear
knows how you do that!'

Dick shook his head.

'Sometimes you can't,' said he reflectively; 'sometimes you're
off the spot altogether. I've heard you say you can't write some
days; and some days a man can't bowl. Ay, you *could* write, and I
could bowl, but they'd smack me to t'boundary over after over.'

'And what I wrote I should tear up next morning.'

He lay looking at the window. It was soft weather now, and a watery sun shone weakly into the room, slanting almost to the bed, so that a bleached and bony hand hung glistening in the rays. I knew that it was itching to hold a ball again – that Dick's spirit was in flannels – even before he continued:

'Now to-day's a day when you could bowl. I'm glad it isn't t'season: it'd be my day, would this, wi' a wet wicket drying from t'top. By gum, but you can do summat wi' a wicket like yon. The ground fairly bites, an' the ball'll come in wi' your arm, or break back or gang, just as it's told; it's the time a ball answers its helm, sir, is that! And it's a rum thing, but it'll drop where you ask it on a bowler's wicket; but on a good one it seems to know that they can make a half-volley of it almost wherever it drops, so it loses heart and pitches all over the shop. Ay, there's a deal o' human natur' in a treble-seam, sir; it don't like getting knocked about any more than we do.'

So we would chat by the hour together, and the present was our favourite tense, as though his cricket days were not nearly over. Nor did I see any sense or kindness in convincing him that they were, and a little persuasion brought Mrs Unthank to my way of thinking and acting in the matter. Clergymen, however, are bound by other considerations, and though Unthank was by no means irreligious, but had an open ear and mind for the manly young curate who came to see him from time to time, he did bitterly complain to me one evening when the curate was gone.

'No game's lost till it's won, sir, and t'parson has no right to shake his head till the umpire gives me out. I don't say I'm in for a long score – bowlers very seldom are, but I isn't going out just yet a bit. I'll get better set by-and-by, and you'll see me trouble the scorers yet.'

It was easy to tell that Dick was proud of his metaphor, and it recurred continually in his talk. His disease was 'the bowler' and each fit of coughing 'a nasty one', but if he could only keep up his wicket till summer-time he felt confident of adding some years to his score. This confidence clung to him almost to the last. He would give up the inn and get back to Bramall Lane, and umpire for 't'owd team' as long as he had a leg to stand on.

I remember when he realized the truth.

In a corner of the best parlour, beneath an accumulation of old newspapers and the ruins of a glass shade, I found one day, when I had finished but was still polishing my book, a war-worn cricket-ball with a tarnished silver plate let into the bruised leather. The inscription on the plate announced that this was the actual ball with which Richard Unthank had taken nine Nottingham wickets (the tenth being run out) for a matter of fifty runs, at Bramall Lane, in his palmy days. That was twenty years ago, but I knew from Dick that it remained the achievement of which he was proudest, and I took the ball upstairs to him after cleaning the silver plate as well as I could with soap and water.

His hot eyes glistened.

'Why, wherever did you find this, sir?' he cried, with the joy of a child in his shallow voice. 'I'd forgot I had it. How canny it feels! Ay, ay, yon was the happiest day in all my life!'

And rapidly and excitedly he gave me full particulars, explaining how and why the wicket had suited him to a nicety, and how he had known before he finished an over that it was his day of days. Then he went through the Notts eleven, and told me with what ball and by what wile he had captured this wicket after that. Only one of the nine had fallen more by luck than good bowling; that was when Dick atoned for a half-volley by holding a terrific return, and so won the match for Yorkshire by the narrow margin of three runs.

'It was my slow ball, and a bit too slow, I doubt, an' he runs out of his ground an' let's drive. There was an almighty crack, and next thing I hears is a rush of air low down to the on. I goes for it wi'out seeing a thing, feels a smack on my hand, an' there's the beautiful ball stuck in it that tight that nobbut gunpowder could ha' shifted her! She looked that sweet and peaceful sticking in my hand that

what do you think I did? Took an' kissed her instead of chucking
her up! You see, sir, I'd forgot that if I'd lost her we should ha' lost
t'match instead o' winning, for she was a dead-sure boundary; when
owd Tom tell'd me it made me feel that bad, I'd got to have a big
drink or faint; an' I feel bad when I think of it yet.'

In his excitement he had raised himself on his left elbow. The
effort had relaxed his muscles, and the historic ball had slipped
from his fingers and was rolling across the floor. I picked it up, and
was about to return it to him, but Dick Unthank waved me back.

'Nay, nay,' said he. 'Give us a catch, sir. They're runnin'!'

So I tossed it gently into his outstretched hand, but the weak
fingers closed too soon, and once more the ball rolled on the floor.
Dick looked at me comically, yet with a spot of colour on either
cheekbone, as he shook his head.

'I doubt I'm out of practice,' he said. 'Come, let's try again.'

'I wouldn't, Dick.'

'You wouldn't? What do you mean? Do you think I'm that bad
I can't catch a cricket ball – me that's played for All England in my
day? Chuck her in again and I'll show you! Get to t'boundary at
t'other side o' t'room!'

He was sitting bolt upright now, with both hands ready, and in
his altered tone there was such umbrage that I could not cross him.
So again I threw; but two such hands were no better than one; the
ball fell through them into the bed; and Dick Unthank sat looking
at me with death dawning in his eyes.

'It's the light,' I said gruffly, for it was the finest day of the New
Year, and even now the sun was glinting on the silver-mounted ball.

'Who could make catches in a light like this?'

'No, sir,' whispered Dick, 'it's not the light. I see what it is. It's
– it's what they call the beginning o' the end.'

And he burst into tears. Yet was he sanguine even then, for the
end was very near. It came that night.

From PSMITH IN THE CITY

BY P. G. WODEHOUSE (1910)

P. G. Wodehouse (1881–1975) needs little introduction. His Jeeves stories are read worldwide and many have now been adapted for television. What is less well known is that he joined the Author's XI alongside such other luminaries as Sir Arthur Conan Doyle. In the early 1900s he wrote several cricketing novels, one of which was *Psmith in the City*, from which the following extract is taken.

* * *

VOLUMES MIGHT HAVE BEEN WRITTEN ON THE CRICKET LUNCH and the influence it has on the run of the game; how it undoes one man, and sends another back to the fray like a giant refreshed; how it turns the brilliant fast bowler into the sluggish medium, and the nervous bat into the masterful smiter.

On Mike its effect was magical. He lunched wisely and well, chewing his food with the concentration of thirty-three-bites a mouthful crank, and drinking ginger-ale. As he walked out with Joe after the interval he knew that a change had taken place in him. His nerve had come back, and with it his form.

From THE MARACOT DEEP AND OTHER STORIES

BY SIR ARTHUR CONAN DOYLE (1929)

Sir Arthur Conan Doyle (1859–1930) was the creator of the greatest detective of them all, the immortal Sherlock Holmes. He was also a cricketer of some ability, having once captured the wicket of W. G. Grace. On another occasion he took seven wickets for 61 runs for the MCC against Cambridgeshire at Lord's. His great love for the game frequently appears in his work; he wrote an essay on W. G. Grace for *The Strand* magazine in 1927, as well as several cricketing short stories. The following tale is an amusing account of Tom Spedegue and his spectacular bowling feat against the Australians.

* * *

THE STORY OF SPEDEGUE'S DROPPER

THE NAME OF WALTER SCOUGALL NEEDS NO INTRODUCTION TO the cricketing public. In the 1890s he played for his University. Early in the century he began that long career in the county team which carried him up to the War. That great tragedy broke his heart for games, but he still served on his county Club Committee and was reckoned one of the best judges of the game in the United Kingdom.

Scougall, after his abandonment of active sport, was wont to take his exercise by long walks through the New Forest, upon the borders of which he was living. Like all wise men, he walked very silently through that wonderful waste, and in that way he was often privileged to see sights which are lost to the average heavy-stepping wayfarer. Once, late in the evening, it was a badger blundering towards its hole under a hollow bank. Often a little group of deer would be glimpsed in the open rides. Occasionally a fox would steal across the path and then dart off at the sight of the noiseless wayfarer. Then one day he saw a human sight which was more strange than any in the animal world. In a narrow glade there stood two great oaks. They were thirty or forty feet apart, and the glade was spanned by a cord which connected them up. This cord was at least fifty feet above the ground, and it must have entailed no small effort to get it there. At each side of the cord a cricket stump had been placed at the usual distance from each other. A tall, thin young man in spectacles was lobbing balls, of which he seemed to have a good supply, from one end, while at the other end a lad of sixteen, wearing wicket-keeper's gloves, was catching those which missed the wicket. 'Catching' is the right word, for no ball struck the ground. Each was projected high up into the air and passed over the cord, descending at a very sharp angle on to the stumps.

Scougall stood for some minutes behind a holly bush watching this curious performance. At first it seemed pure lunacy, and then gradually he began to perceive a method in it. It was no easy matter to hurl a ball up over that cord and bring it down near the wicket. It needed a very correct trajectory. And yet this singular young man, using what the observer's practised eye recognized as a leg-break action which would entail a swerve in the air, lobbed up ball after ball either right on to the bails or into the wicket-keeper's hands just beyond them. Great practice was surely needed before he had attained such a degree of accuracy as this.

Finally his curiosity became so great that Scougall moved into the glade, to the obvious surprise and embarrassment of the two performers. Had they been caught in some guilty action they could not have looked more unhappy. However, Scougall was a man of the world with a pleasant manner, and he soon put them at their ease.

'Excuse my butting in,' said he. 'I happened to be passing and I could not help being interested. I am an old cricketer, you see, and it appealed to me. Might I ask what you were trying to do?'

'Oh, I am just tossing up a few balls,' said the elder, modestly. 'You see, there is no decent ground about here, so my brother and I come out into the Forest.'

'Are you a bowler, then?'

'Well, of sorts.'

'What club do you play for?'

'It is only Wednesday and Saturday cricket. Bishops Bramley is our village.'

'But do you always bowl like that?'

'Oh, no. This is a new idea that I have been trying out.'

'Well, you seem to get it pretty accurately.'

'I am improving. I was all over the place at first. I didn't know what parish they would drop in. But now they are usually there or about it.'

'So I observe.'

'You said you were an old cricketer. May I ask your name?'

'Walter Scougall.'

The young man looked at him as a young pupil looks at the world-famed master.

'You remember the name, I see.'

'Walter Scougall. Oxford and Hampshire. Last played in 1913. Batting average for that season, 27.5. Bowling average, 16 for 72 wickets.'

'Good Lord!'

The younger man, who had come across, burst out laughing.

'Tom is like that,' said he. 'He is Wisden and Lillywhite rolled into one. He could tell you anyone's record, and every county's record for this century.'

'Well, well. What a memory you must have!'

'Well, my heart is in the game,' said the young man, becoming amazingly confidential, as shy men will when they find a really sympathetic listener. 'But it's my heart that won't let me play it as I should wish to do. You see, I get asthma if I do too much – and palpitations. But they play me at Bishops Bramley for my slow bowling, and so long as I field slip I don't have too much running to do.'

'You say you have not tried these lobs, or whatever you may call them, in a match?'

'No, not yet. I want to get them perfect first. You see, it was my ambition to invent an entirely new ball. I am sure it can be done. Look at Bosanquet and the googly. Just by using his brain he thought of and worked out the idea of concealed screw on the ball. I said to myself that Nature had handicapped me with a weak heart, but not with a weak brain, and that I might think out some new thing which was within the compass of my strength. Droppers, I call them. Spedegue's droppers – that's the name they may have some day.'

Scougall laughed. 'I don't want to discourage you, but I wouldn't bank on it too much,' said he. 'A quick-eyed batsman would simply treat them as he would any other full toss and every ball would be a boundary.'

Spedegue's face fell. The words of Scougall were to him as the verdict of the High Court judge. Never had he spoken before with a first-class cricketer, and he had hardly the nerve to defend his own theory. It was the younger one who spoke.

'Perhaps, Mr Scougall, you have hardly thought it all out yet,' said he. 'Tom has given it a lot of consideration. You see, if the ball is tossed high enough it has a great pace as it falls. It's really like having a fast bowler from above. That's his idea. Then, of course, there's the field.'

'Ah, how would you place your field?'

'All on the on side bar one or two at the most,' cried Tom Spedegue, taking up the argument. 'I've nine to dispose of. I should have mid-off well up. That's all. Then I should have eight men to leg, three on the boundary, one mid-on, two square, one fine, and one a rover, so that the batsman would never quite know where he was. That's the idea.'

Scougall began to be serious. It was clear that this young fellow really had plotted the thing out. He walked across to the wicket.

'Chuck up one or two,' said he. 'Let me see how they look.' He brandished his walking-stick and waited expectant. The ball soared in the air and came down with unexpected speed just over the stump. Scougall looked more serious still. He had seen many cricket balls, but never quite from that angle, and it gave him food for thought.

'Have you ever tried it in public?'

'Never.'

'Don't you think it is about time?'

'Yes, I think I might.'

'When?'

'Well, I'm not generally on as a first bowler. I am second change as a rule. But if the skipper will let me have a go…'

'I'll see to that,' said Scougall. 'Do you play at Bishops Bramley?'

'Yes; it is our match of the year – against Mudford, you know.'

'Well, I think on Saturday I'd like to be there and see how it works.'

Sure enough Scougall turned up at the village match, to the great excitement of the two rural teams. He had a serious talk with the home captain, with the result that for the first time in his life Tom Spedegue was first bowler for his native village. What the other village thought of his remarkable droppers need not influence us much, since they would probably have been got out pretty cheaply by any sort of bowling. None the less, Scougall watched the procession to and from the cow-shed which served as a pavilion with an appreciative eye, and his views as to the possibilities lying in the dropper became clearer than before. At the end of the innings he touched the bowler upon the shoulder.

'That seems all right,' he said.

'No, I couldn't quite get the length – and, of course, they did drop catches.'

'Yes, I agree that you could do better. Now look here! you are second master at a school, are you not?'

'That is right.'

'You could get a day's leave if I wangled with the chief?'

'It might be done.'

'Well, I want you next Tuesday. Sir George Sanderson's house-party team is playing the Free Foresters at Ringwood. You must bowl for Sir George.'

Tom Spedegue flushed with pleasure. 'Oh, I say!' was all he could stammer out.

'I'll work it somehow or other. I suppose you don't bat?'

'Average nine,' said Spedegue, proudly.

Scougall laughed. 'Well, I noticed that you were not a bad fielder near the wicket.'

'I usually hold them.'

'Well, I'll see your boss, and you will hear from me again.'

Scougall was really taking a great deal of trouble in this small affair, for he went down to Totton and saw the rather grim head master. It chanced, however, that the old man had been a bit of a sport in his day, and he relaxed when Scougall explained the inner meaning of it all. He laughed incredulously, however, and shook his head when Scougall whispered some aspiration.

'Nonsense!' was his comment.

'Well, there is a chance.'

'Nonsense!' said the old man once again.

'It would be the making of your school.'

'It certainly would,' the head master replied. 'But it is nonsense all the same.'

Scougall saw the head master again on the morning after the Free Foresters match.

'You see it works all right,' he said.

'Yes, against third-class men.'

'Oh, I don't know. Donaldson was playing, and Murphy. They

were not so bad. I tell you they are the most amazed set of men in Hampshire. I have bound them all over to silence.'

'Why?'

'Surprise is the essence of the matter. Now I'll take it a stage farther. By Jove, what a joke it would be!' The old cricketer and the sporting schoolmaster roared with laughter as they thought of the chances of the future.

All England was absorbed in one question at that moment. Politics, business, even taxation had passed from people's minds. The one engrossing subject was the fifth Test Match. Twice England had won by a narrow margin, and twice Australia had barely struggled to victory. Now in a week Lord's was to be the scene of the final and crucial battle of giants. What were the chances, and how was the English team to be made up?

It was an anxious time for the Selection Committee, and three more harassed men than Sir James Gilpin, Mr Tarding and Dr Sloper were not to be found in London. They sat now in the committee room of the great pavilion, and they moodily scanned the long list of possibles which lay before them, weighing the claims of this man or that, closely inspecting the latest returns from the county matches, and arguing how far a good all-rounder was a better bargain than a man who was supremely good in one department but weak in another – such men, for example, as Worsley of Lancashire, whose average was seventy-one, but who was a sluggard in the field, or Scott of Leicestershire, who was near the top of the bowling and quite at the foot of the batting averages. A week of such work had turned the committee into three jaded old men.

'There is the question of endurance,' said Sir James, the man of many years and much experience. 'A three days' match is bad enough, but this is to be played out and may last a week. Some of these top average men are getting on in years.'

'Exactly,' said Tarding, who had himself captained England again and again. 'I am all for young blood and new methods. The trouble is that we know their bowling pretty well, and as for them on a marled wicket they can play ours with their eyes shut. Each side is likely to make five hundred per innings, and a very little will make the difference between us and them.'

'It's just that very little that we have got to find,' said solemn old Dr Sloper, who had the reputation of being the greatest living authority upon the game. 'If we could give them something new! But, of course, they have played every county and sampled everything we have got.'

'What can we ever have that is new?' cried Tarding. 'It is all played out.'

'Well, I don't know,' said Sir James. 'Both the swerve and the googly have come along in our time. But Bosanquets don't appear every day. We want brain as well as muscle behind the ball.'

'Funny we should talk like this,' said Dr Sloper, taking a letter from his pocket. 'This is from old Scougall, down in Hampshire. He says he is at the end of a wire and is ready to come up if we want him. His whole argument is on the very lines we have been discussing. New blood, and a complete surprise – that is his slogan.'

'Does he suggest where we are to find it?'

'Well, as a matter of fact he does. He has dug up some unknown fellow from the back of beyond who plays for the second eleven of the Mudtown Blackbeetles or the Hinton Chawbacons or some such team, and he wants to put him straight in to play for England. Poor old Scougie has been out in the sun.'

'At the same time there is no better captain than Scougall used to be. I don't think we should put his opinion aside too easily. What does he say?'

'Well, he is simply red-hot about it. "A revelation to me." That is one phrase. "Could not have believed it if I had not seen it." "May find it out afterwards, but it is bound to upset them the first time." That is his view.'

'And where is this wonder man?'

'He has sent him up so that we can see him if we wish. Telephone the Thackeray Hotel, Bloomsbury.'

'Well, what do you say?'

'Oh, it's a pure waste of time,' said Tarding. 'Such things don't happen, you know. Even if we approved of him, what would the country think and what would the Press say?'

Sir James stuck out his grizzled jaw. 'Damn the country and the Press, too!' said he. 'We are here to follow our own judgement, and I jolly well mean to do so.'

'Exactly,' said Dr Sloper.

Tarding shrugged his broad shoulders. 'We have enough to do without turning down a side-street like that,' said he. 'However, if you both think so, I won't stand in the way. Have him up by all means and let us see what we make of him.'

Half an hour later a very embarrassed young man was standing in front of the famous trio and listening to a series of very searching questions, to which he was giving such replies as he was able. Much of the ground which Scougall had covered in the Forest was explored by them once more.

'It boils down to this, Mr Spedegue. You've once in your life played in good company. That is the only criterion. What exactly did you do?'

Spedegue pulled a slip of paper, which was already frayed from much use, out of his waistcoat pocket. 'This is *The Hampshire Telegraph* account, sir.'

Sir James ran his eye over it and read snatches aloud. '"Much amusement was caused by the bowling of Mr T. E. Spedegue." Hum! That's rather two-edged. Bowling should not be a comic turn. After all, cricket is a serious game. Seven wickets for thirty-four. Well, that's better. Donaldson is a good man. You got him, I see. And Murphy, too! Well, now, would you mind going into the pavilion and waiting? You will find some pictures there that will amuse you if you value the history of the game. We'll send for you presently.'

When the youth had gone the Selection Committee looked at each other in puzzled silence.

'You simply can't do it!' said Tarding at last. 'You can't face it. To play a bumpkin like that because he once got seven wickets for thirty-four in country-house cricket is sheer madness. I won't be a party to it.'

'Wait a bit, though! Wait a bit!' cried Sir James. 'Let us thresh it out a little before we decide.'

So they threshed it out, and in half an hour they sent for Tom Spedegue once more. Sir James sat with his elbows on the table and his finger-tips touching while he held forth in his best judicial manner. His conclusion was a remarkable one.

'So it comes to this, Mr Spedegue, that we all three want to be on surer ground before we take a step which would rightly expose us to the most tremendous public criticism. You will therefore remain in London, and at three-forty-five tomorrow morning, which is just after dawn, you will come down in your flannels to the side entrance of Lord's. We will, under the pledge of secrecy, assemble twelve or thirteen groundmen whom we can trust, including half-a-dozen first-class bats. We will have a wicket prepared on the practice ground, and we will try you out under proper conditions with your ten fielders and all. If you fail, there is an end. If you make good, we may consider your claim.'

'Good gracious, sir, I made no claim.'

'Well, your friend Scougall did for you. But anyhow, that's how we have fixed it. We shall be there, of course, and a few others whose opinion we can trust. If you care to wire Scougall he can come too. But the whole thing is secret, for we quite see the point that it must be a complete surprise or a wash-out. So you will keep your mouth shut and we shall do the same.'

Thus it came about that one of the most curious games in the history of cricket was played on the Lord's ground next morning. There is a high wall round that part, but early wayfarers as they passed were amazed to hear the voices of the players, and the occasional crack of the ball at such an hour. The superstitious might almost have imagined that the spirits of the great departed were once again at work, and that the adventurous explorer might get a peep at the bushy black beard of the old giant or Billie Murdoch leading his Cornstalks once more to victory. At six o'clock the impromptu match was over, and the Selection Committee had taken the bravest and most sensational decision that had ever been hazarded since first a team was chosen. Tom Spedegue should play next week for England.

'Mind you,' said Tarding, 'if the beggar lets us down I simply won't face the music. I warn you of that. I'll have a taxi waiting at the gate and a passport in my pocket. Poste restante, Paris. That's me for the rest of the summer.'

'Cheer up, old chap,' said Sir James. 'Our conscience is clear. We have acted for the best. Dash it all, we have ten good men, anyhow. If the worst came to the worst, it only means one passenger in the team.'

'But it won't come to the worst,' said Dr Sloper, stoutly. 'Hang it, we have seen with our own eyes. What more can we do? All the same, for the first time in my life I'll have a whisky-and-soda before breakfast.'

Next day the list was published and the buzz began. Ten of the men might have been expected. These were Challen and Jones, as fast bowlers, and Widley, the slow left-hander. Then Peters, Moir, Jackson, Wilson and Grieve were at the head of the batting averages, none of them under fifty, which was pretty good near the close of a wet season. Hanwell and Gordon were two all-rounders who were always sure of their places, dangerous bats, good change bowlers, and as active as cats in the field. So far so good. But who the Evil One was Thomas E. Spedegue? Never was there such a ferment in Fleet Street and such blank ignorance upon the part of 'our well-informed correspondent'. Special Commissioners darted here and there, questioning well-known cricketers, only to find that they were as much in the dark as themselves. Nobody knew – or if anyone did know, he was bound by oath not to tell. The wildest tales flew abroad.

'We are able to assure the public that Spedegue is a "nom de jeu" and conceals the identity of a world-famed cricketer who for family reasons is not permitted to reveal his true self.' 'Thomas E. Spedegue will surprise the crowd at Lord's by appearing as a coal-black gentleman from Jamaica. He came over with the last West Indian team, settled in Derbyshire, and is now eligible to play for England, though why he should be asked to do so is still a mystery.' 'Spedegue, as is now generally known, is a half-caste Malay who exhibited extraordinary cricket proficiency some years ago in Rangoon. It is said that he plays in a loincloth and can catch as well with his feet as with his hands. The question of whether he is qualified for England is a most debatable one.' 'Spedegue, Thomas E., is the headmaster of a famous northern school whose wonderful talents in the cricket field have been concealed by his devotion to his academic duties. Those who know him best are assured,' etc., etc.

The Committee also began to get it in the neck. 'Why, with the wealth of talent available, these three elderly gentlemen, whose ideas of selection seem to be to pick names out of a bag, should choose one who, whatever his hidden virtues, is certainly unused to first-class cricket, far less to Test Matches, is one of those things which make one realize that the lunacy laws are not sufficiently comprehensive.' These were fair samples of the comments. And then the inevitable came to pass. When Fleet Street is out for something it invariably gets it. No one quite knows how *The Daily Sportsman* succeeded in getting at Thomas Spedegue, but it was a great scoop and the incredible secret was revealed. There was a leader and there was an interview with the village patriarch which set London roaring with laughter. 'No, we ain't surprised nohow,' said Gaffer Hobbs. 'Maister Spedegue do be turble clever with them slow balls of his'n. He sure was too much for them chaps what came in the char-à-bancs from Mudford. Artful, I call him.

You'll see.' The leader was scathing. 'The Committee certainly seem to have taken leave of their senses. Perhaps there is time even now to alter their absurd decision. It is almost an insult to our Australian visitors. It is obvious that the true place for Mr Thomas Spedegue, however artful he may be, is the village green and not Lord's, and that his competence to deal with the char-à-bancers of Mudford is a small guarantee that he can play first-class cricket. The whole thing is a deplorable mistake, and it is time that pressure was put upon the Selection Board to make them reconsider their decision.'

'We have examined the score-book of the Bishops Bramley village club,' wrote another critic. 'It is kept in the tap-room of The Spotted Cow, and makes amusing reading. Our Test Match aspirant is hard to trace, as he played usually for the second eleven, and in any case there was no one capable of keeping an analysis. However, we must take such comfort as we can from his batting averages. This year he has actually amassed a hundred runs in nine recorded innings. Best in an innings, fifteen. Average, eleven. Last year he was less fortunate and came out with an average of nine. The youth is second master at the Totton High School and is in indifferent health, suffering from occasional attacks of asthma. And he is chosen to play for England! Is it a joke or what? We think that the public will hardly see the humour of it, nor will the Selection Committee find it a laughing matter if they persist in their preposterous action.'

So spoke the Press, but there were, it is only fair to say, other journals which took a more charitable view. 'After all,' said the sporting correspondent of *The Times*, 'Sir James and his two colleagues are old and experienced players with a unique knowledge of the game. Since we have placed our affairs in their hands we must be content to leave them there. They have their own knowledge and their own private information of which we are ignorant. We can but trust them and await the event.'

As to the three, they refused in any way to compromise or to

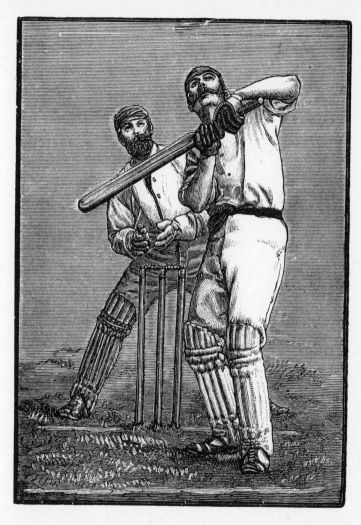

bend to the storm. They gave no explanations, made no excuses, and simply dug in and lay quiet. So the world waited till the day came round.

We all remember what glorious weather it was. The heat and the perfect Bulli-earth wicket, so far as England could supply that commodity, reminded our visitors of their native conditions. It was

England, however, who got the best of that ironed shirt-front
wicket, for in their first knock even Cotsmore, the Australian giant,
who was said to be faster than Gregory and more wily than
Spofforth, could seldom get the ball bail-high. He bowled with
splendid vim and courage, but his analysis at the end of the day
only showed three wickets for a hundred and forty-two. Storr, the
googly merchant, had a better showing with four for ninety-six.
Cade's mediums accounted for two wickets, and Moir, the English
captain, was run out. He had made seventy-three first, and Peters,
Grieve, and Hanwell raked up sixty-four, fifty-seven, and fifty-one
respectively, while nearly everyone was in double figures. The only
exception was 'Thomas E. Spedegue, Esq.,' to quote the score card,
which recorded a blank after his name. He was caught in the slips
off the fast bowler, and, as he admitted afterwards that he had
never for an instant seen the ball, and could hardly in his
nervousness see the bowler, it is remarkable that his wicket was
intact. The English total was four hundred and thirty-two, and the
making of it consumed the whole of the first day. It was fast
scoring in the time, and the crowd were fully satisfied with the
result.

And now came the turn of Australia. An hour before play
began forty thousand people had assembled, and by the time that
the umpires came out the gates had to be closed, for there was not
standing room within those classic precincts. Then came the
English team, strolling out to the wickets and tossing the ball from
hand to hand in time-honoured fashion. Finally appeared the two
batsmen, Morland, the famous Victorian, the man of the quick
feet and the supple wrists, whom many looked upon as the premier
batsman of the world, and the stonewaller, Donahue, who had
broken the hearts of so many bowlers with his obdurate defence. It
was he who took the first over, which was delivered by Challen of
Yorkshire, the raging, tearing fast bowler of the North. He sent
down six beauties, but each of them came back to him down the
pitch from that impenetrable half-cock shot which was

characteristic of the famous Queenslander. It was a maiden over.

And now Moir tossed the ball to Spedegue and motioned him to begin at the pavilion end. The English captain had been present at the surreptitious trial and he had an idea of the general programme, but it took him some time and some consultation with the nervous, twitching bowler before he could set the field. When it was finally arranged the huge audience gasped with surprise and the batsmen gazed round them as if they could hardly believe their eyes. One poor little figure, alone upon a prairie, broke the solitude of the off-side. He stood as a deep point or as a silly mid-off. The on-side looked like a mass meeting. The fielders were in each other's way, and kept shuffling about to open up separate lines. It took some time to arrange, while Spedegue stood at the crease with a nervous smile, fingering the ball and waiting for orders. The Selection Board were grouped in the open window of the committee-room, and their faces were drawn and haggard.

'My God! This is awful!' muttered Tarding.

'Got that cab?' asked Dr Sloper, with a ghastly smile.

'Got it! It is my one stand-by.'

'Room for three in it?' said Sir James. 'Gracious, he has got five short-legs and no slip. Well, well, get to it! Anything is better than waiting.'

There was a deadly hush as Spedegue delivered his first ball. It was an ordinary slow full pitch straight on the wicket. At any other time Morland would have slammed it to the boundary, but he was puzzled and cautious after all this mysterious setting of the field. Some unknown trap seemed to have been set for him. Therefore he played the ball quietly back to the bowler and set himself for the next one, which was similar and treated the same way.

Spedegue had lost his nerve. He simply could not, before this vast multitude of critics, send up the grotesque ball which he had invented. Therefore he compromised, which was the most fatal of all courses. He lobbed up balls which were high but not high enough. They were simply ordinary over-pitched, full-toss deliveries such as a batsman sees when he has happy dreams and smiles in his sleep. Such was the third ball, which was a little to the off. Morland sent it like a bullet past the head of the lonely mid-off and it crashed against the rails. The three men in the window looked at each other and the sweat was on their brows. The next ball was again a juicy full toss on the level of the batsman's ribs. He banged it through the crowd of fielders on the on with a deft turn of the wrist which insured that it should be upon the ground. Then, gaining confidence, he waited for the next of those wonderful dream balls, and steadying himself for a mighty fast-footed swipe he knocked it clean over the ring and on to the roof of the hotel to square-leg. There were roars of applause, for a British crowd loves a lofty hit, whoever may deliver it. The scoreboard marked fourteen made off five balls. Such an opening to a Test Match had never been seen.

'We thought he might break a record, and by Jove he has!' said Tarding, bitterly. Sir James chewed his ragged moustache and Sloper twisted his fingers together in agony. Moir, who was fielding at mid-on, stepped across to the unhappy bowler.

'Chuck them up, as you did on Tuesday morning. Buck up, man! Don't funk it! You'll do them yet.'

Spedegue grasped the ball convulsively and nerved himself to send it high into the air. For a moment he pictured the New Forest glade, the white line of cord, and his young brother waiting behind the stump. But his nerve was gone, and with it his accuracy. There were roars of laughter as the ball went fifty feet into the air, which were redoubled when the wicket-keeper had to sprint back in order to catch it and the umpire stretched his arms out to signal a wide.

For the last ball, as he realized, that he was likely to bowl in the match, Spedegue approached the crease. The field was swimming round him. That yell of laughter which had greeted his effort had been the last straw. His nerve was broken. But there is a point when pure despair and desperation come to a man's aid – when he says to himself, 'Nothing matters now. All is lost. It can't be worse than

it is. Therefore I may as well let myself go.' Never in all his practice
had he bowled a ball as high as the one which now, to the amused
delight of the crowd, went soaring into the air. Up it went and up –
the most absurd ball ever delivered in a cricket match. The umpire
broke down and shrieked with laughter, while even the amazed
fielders joined in the general yell. The ball, after its huge parabola,
descended well over the wicket, but as it was still within reach
Morland, with a broad grin on his sunburned face, turned round
and tapped it past the wicket-keeper's ear to the boundary.
Spedegue's face drooped towards the ground. The bitterness of
death was on him. It was all over. He had let down the Committee,
he had let down the side, he had let down England. He wished the
ground would open and swallow him so that his only memorial
should be a scar upon the pitch of Lord's.

And then suddenly the derisive laughter of the crowd was
stilled, for it was seen that an incredible thing had happened.
Morland was walking towards the pavilion. As he passed Spedegue
he made a good-humoured flourish of his bat as if he would hit
him over the head with it. At the same time the wicket-keeper
stooped and picked something off the ground. It was a bail.
Forgetful of his position and with all his thoughts upon this
extraordinary ball which was soaring over his head, the great
batsman had touched the wicket with his toe. Spedegue had a
respite. The laughter was changing to applause. Moir came over
and clapped him jovially upon the back. The scoring board showed
total fifteen, last man fourteen, wickets one.

Challen sent down another over of fizzers to the impenetrable
Donahue which resulted in a snick for two and a boundary off his
legs. And then off the last ball a miracle occurred. Spedegue was
fielding at fine slip, when he saw a red flash come towards him low
on the right. He thrust out a clutching hand and there was the
beautiful new ball right in the middle of his tingling palm. How it
got there he had no idea, but what odds so long as the stonewaller
would stonewall no more? Spedegue, from being the butt, was

becoming the hero of the crowd. They cheered rapturously when he approached the crease for his second over. The board was twenty-one, six, two. But now it was a different Spedegue. His fears had fallen from him. His confidence had returned. If he did nothing more he had at least done his share. But he would do much more. It had all come back to him, his sense of distance, his delicacy of delivery, his appreciation of curves. He had found his strength and he meant to keep it.

The splendid Australian batsmen, those active, clear-eyed men who could smile at our fast bowling and make the best of our slow bowlers seem simple, were absolutely at sea. Here was something of which they had never heard, for which they had never prepared, and which was unlike anything in the history of cricket. Spedegue had got his fifty-foot trajectory to a nicety, bowling over the wicket with a marked curve from the leg. Every ball fell on or near the top of the stumps. He was as accurate as a human howitzer pitching shells. Batten, who followed Morland, hit across one of them and was clean bowled. Staker tried to cut one off his wicket, and knocked down his own off-stump, broke his bat, and finally saw the ball descend amid the general *debris*. Here and there one was turned to leg and once a short one was hit out of the ground. The fast bowler sent the fifth batsman's leg-stump flying and the score was five for thirty-seven. Then in successive balls Spedegue got Bollard and Whitelaw, the one caught at the wicket and the other at short square-leg. There was a stand between Moon and Carter, who put on twenty runs between them with a succession of narrow escapes from the droppers. Then each of them became victims, one getting his body in front, and the other being splendidly caught by Hanwell on the ropes. The last man was run out and the innings closed for seventy-four . . .

Well, it was a wonderful day and it came to a wonderful close. It is a matter of history how the crowd broke the ropes, how they flooded the field, and how Spedegue, protesting loudly, was carried shoulder-high into the pavilion. Then came the cheering and the speeches. The hero of the day had to appear again and again. When they were weary of cheering him they cheered for Bishops Bramley. Then the English captain had to make a speech. 'Rather stand up to Cotsmore bowling on a ploughed field,' said he. Then it was the turn of Batten, the Australian. 'You've beat us at something,' he said ruefully; 'don't quite know yet what it is. It's not what we call cricket down under.' Then the Selection Board were called for and they had the heartiest and best deserved cheer of them all. Tarding told them about the waiting cab. 'It's waiting yet,' he said, 'but I think I can now dismiss it.'

Spedegue played no more cricket. His heart would not stand it. His doctor declared that this one match had been one too many and that he must stand out in the future. But for good or for bad – for bad, as many think – he has left his mark upon the game for ever. The English were more amused than exultant over their surprise victory. The Australian papers were at first inclined to be resentful, but then the absurdity that a man from the second eleven of an unknown club should win a Test Match began to soak into them, and finally Sydney and Melbourne had joined London in its appreciation of the greatest joke in the history of cricket.

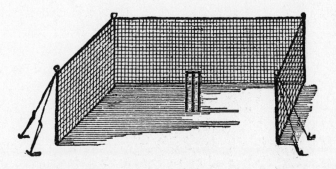

From ENGLAND, THEIR ENGLAND

BY A. G. MACDONELL (1933)

Archibald Gordon Macdonell (1895–1941) is an unlikely candidate
for writing a book about England, having been born on the other
side of the border, in Aberdeen. However he was educated at
Winchester and later lived in the South of England where he would
watch cricket regularly and even on occasion play himself. The
following extract is a classic of cricketing literature, and one which
never fails to make me smile.

* * *

THE CRICKET MATCH

'DON'T FORGET SATURDAY MORNING CHARING CROSS
Underground Station,' ran the telegram which arrived at
Royal Avenue during the week, 'at ten-fifteen sharp. Whatever you
do don't be late. Hodge.'

Saturday morning was bright and sunny, and at ten minutes
past ten Donald arrived at the Embankment entrance of Charing
Cross Underground Station, carrying a small suitcase full of
clothes suitable for outdoor sports and pastimes. He was glad that
he had arrived too early, for it would have been a dreadful thing for
a stranger and a foreigner to have kept such a distinguished man
and his presumably distinguished colleagues even for an instant
from their national game. Laying his bag down on the pavement
and putting one foot upon it carefully – for Donald had heard
stories of the surpassing dexterity of metropolitan thieves – he
waited eagerly for the hands of a neighbouring clock to mark the
quarter past. At twenty minutes to eleven an effeminate-looking
young man, carrying a cricketing bag and wearing a pale-blue silk

jumper up to his ears, sauntered up, remarked casually, 'You
playing?' and, on receiving an answer in the affirmative, dumped
his bag at Donald's feet and said, 'Keep an eye on that like a good
fellow. I'm going to get a shave', and sauntered off round the
corner.

At five minutes to eleven there was a respectable muster, six of
the team having assembled. But at five minutes past a disintegrating
element was introduced by the arrival of Mr Harcourt with the
news, which he announced with the air of a shipwrecked mariner
who has, after twenty-five years of vigilance, seen a sail, that in the
neighbourhood of Charing Cross the pubs opened at eleven
o'clock. So that when Mr Hodge himself turned up at twenty-five
minutes past eleven, resplendent in flannels, a red-and-white
football shirt with a lace-up collar, and a blazer of purple-and-
yellow stripes, each stripe being at least two inches across, and
surmounted by a purple-and-yellow cap that made him somehow
reminiscent of one of the Michelin twins, if not both, he was
justly indignant at the slackness of his team.

'They've no sense of time,' he told Donald repeatedly. 'We're
late as it is. The match is due to begin at half-past eleven, and it's
fifty miles from here. I should have been here myself two hours
ago, but I had my Sunday article to do. It really is too bad.'

When the team, now numbering nine men, had been extricated
from the tavern and had been marshalled on the pavement,
counted, recounted, and the missing pair identified, it was pointed
out by the casual youth who had returned, shining and pomaded
from the barber, that the char-à-banc had not yet arrived.

Mr Hodge's indignation became positively alarming and he
covered the twenty yards to the public telephone box almost as
quickly as Mr Harcourt covered the forty yards back to the door
of the pub. Donald remained on the pavement to guard the heap of
suitcases, cricket bags, and stray equipment – one player had
arrived with a pair of flannels rolled in a tight ball under his arm
and a left-hand batting glove, while another had contributed a

cardboard box which he had bought at Hamley's on the way down, and which contained six composite cricket balls, boys' size, and a pair of bails. It was just as well that Donald did remain on guard, partly because no one else seemed to care whether the luggage was stolen or not, partly because Mr Hodge emerged in a perfect frenzy a minute or two later from the telephone-box to borrow two pennies to put in the slot, and partly because by the time the telephone call was at last in full swing and Mr Hodge's command over the byways of British invective was enjoying complete freedom of action, the char-à-banc rolled up beside the kerb.

At twelve-thirty it was decided not to wait for the missing pair, and the nine cricketers started off. At two-thirty, after halts at Catford, the White Hart at Sevenoaks, the Angel at Tunbridge Wells, and three smaller inns at tiny villages, the char-à-banc drew up triumphantly beside the cricket ground of the Kentish village of Fordenden. Donald was enchanted at his first real sight of rural England. And rural England is the real England, unspoilt by factories and financiers and tourists and hustle. He sprang out of the char-à-banc, in which he had been tightly wedged between a very stout publisher who had laughed all the way down and had quivered at each laugh like the needle of a seismograph during one of Japan's larger earthquakes, and a youngish and extremely learned professor of ballistics, and gazed eagerly round. The sight was worth an eager gaze or two.

It was a hot summer's afternoon. There was no wind, and the smoke from the red-roofed cottages curled slowly up into the golden haze. The clock on the flint tower of the church struck the half-hour, and the vibrations spread slowly across the shimmering hedgerows, spangled with white blossom of the convolvulus, and lost themselves tremulously among the orchards. Bees lazily drifted. White butterflies flapped their aimless way among the gardens. Delphiniums, larkspur, tiger-lilies, evening primrose, monk's hood, sweet peas, swaggered brilliantly above the box hedges, the wooden palings and the rickety gates. The cricket field itself was a mass of daisies and buttercups and dandelions, tall grasses and purple vetches and thistledown, and great clumps of dark-red sorrel, except, of course, for the oblong patch in the centre – mown, rolled, watered – a smooth, shining emerald of grass, the pride of Fordenden, the Wicket.

The entire scene was perfect to the last detail. It was as if Mr Cochran had, with his spectacular genius, brought Ye Olde Englyshe Village straight down by special train from the London Pavilion, complete with synthetic cobwebs (from the Wigan factory), hand-made smocks for ye gaffers (called in the cabaret scenes and the North-West Mounted Police scenes, the Gentlemen of the Singing Ensemble), and aluminium Eezi-Milk stools for the dairymaids (or Ladies of the Dancing Ensemble). For there stood the vicar, beaming absentmindedly at everyone. There was the forge, with the blacksmith, his hammer discarded, tightening his snake-buckled belt for the fray and loosening his braces to enable his terrific bowling arm to swing freely in its socket. There on a long bench outside the Three Horseshoes sat a row of elderly men, facing a row of pint tankards, and wearing either long beards or clean-shaven chins and long whiskers. Near them, holding pint tankards in their hands, was another group of men, clustered together and talking with intense animation. Donald thought that

one or two of them seemed familiar, but it was not until he turned
back to the char-à-banc to ask if he could help with the luggage
that he realized that they were Mr Hodge and his team already
sampling the proprietor's wares. (A notice above the door of the
inn stated that the proprietor's name was A. Bason and that he was
licensed to sell wines, spirits, beers and tobacco.)

All round the cricket field small parties of villagers were
patiently waiting for the great match to begin – a match against
gentlemen from London is an event in a village – and some of
them looked as if they had been waiting for a good long time. But
they were not impatient. Village folk are very seldom impatient.
Those whose lives are occupied in combating the eccentricities of
God regard as very small beer the eccentricities of man.

Blue-and-green dragonflies played at hide-and-seek among the
thistledown, and a pair of swans flew overhead. An ancient man
leaned upon a scythe, his sharpening-stone sticking out of a pocket
in his velveteen waistcoat. A magpie flapped lazily across the
meadows. The parson shook hands with the squire. Doves cooed.
The haze flickered. The world stood still.

At twenty minutes to three Mr Hodge had completed his
rather tricky negotiations with the Fordenden captain and had
arranged that two substitutes should be lent by Fordenden in order
that the visitors should field eleven men, and that nine men on
each side should bat. But just as the two men on the Fordenden
side, who had been detailed for the unpleasant duty of fielding for
both sides and batting for neither, had gone off home in high
dudgeon, a motor-car arrived containing not only Mr Hodge's two
defaulters but a third gentleman in flannels as well, who swore
stoutly that he had been invited by Mr Hodge to play and affirmed
that he was jolly well going to play. Whoever stood down, it wasn't
going to be him. Negotiations therefore had to be reopened, the
pair of local Achilles had to be recalled, and at ten minutes to
three the match began upon a twelve-a-side basis.

Mr Hodge, having won the toss by a system of his own

founded upon the differential calculus and the Copernican theory, sent in his opening pair to bat. One was James Livingstone, a very sound club cricketer, and the other one was called, simply, Boone. Boone was a huge, awe-inspiring colossus of a man, weighing at least eighteen stone and wearing all the majestic trappings of a Cambridge Blue. Donald felt that it was hardly fair to loose such cracks upon a humble English village until he fortunately remembered that he, of all people, a foreigner, admitted by courtesy to the National Game, ought not to set himself up to be a judge of what is, and what is not, cricket.

The Fordenden team ranged themselves at the bidding of their captain, the Fordenden baker, in various spots of vantage amid the daisies, buttercups, dandelions, vetches, thistledown and clumps of dark-red sorrel; and the blacksmith, having taken in, just for luck as it were, yet another reef in his snake-buckle belt, prepared to open the attack. It so happened that at the end at which he was to bowl the ground behind the wicket was level for a few yards and then sloped away rather abruptly, so that it was only during the last three or four intensive, galvanic yards of his run that the blacksmith, who took a long run, was visible to the batsman or indeed to anyone on the field of play except the man stationed in the deep field behind him. This man saw nothing of the game except the blacksmith walking back dourly and the blacksmith running up ferociously, and occasionally a ball driven smartly over the brow of the hill in his direction.

The sound club player having taken guard, having twiddled his bat round several times in a nonchalant manner, and having stared arrogantly at each fieldsman in turn, was somewhat surprised to find that, although the field was ready, no bowler was visible. His doubts, however, were resolved a second or two later, when the blacksmith came up, breasting the slope superbly like a mettlesome combination of Vulcan and Venus Anadyomene. The first ball which he delivered was a high full-pitch to leg, of appalling velocity. It must have lighted up a bare patch among the long grass near long-leg, for it rocketed, first bounce, into the hedge and four byes were reluctantly signalled by the village umpire. The row of gaffers on the rustic bench shook their heads, agreed that it was many years since four byes had been signalled on that ground, and called for more pints of old-and-mild. The other members of Mr Hodge's team blanched visibly and called for more pints of bitter. The youngish professor of ballistics, who was in next, muttered something about muzzle velocities and started to do a sum on the back of an envelope.

The second ball went full-pitch into the wicketkeeper's stomach and there was a delay while the deputy wicketkeeper was invested with the pads and gloves of office. The third ball, making a noise like a partridge, would have hummed past Mr Livingstone's left ear had he not dexterously struck it out of the ground for six, and the fourth took his leg bail with a bullet-like full-pitch. Ten runs for one wicket, last man 6. The professor got the fifth ball on the left ear and went back to the Three Horseshoes, while Mr Harcourt had the singular misfortune to hit his wicket before the sixth ball was even delivered. Ten runs for two wickets and one man retired hurt. A slow left-hand bowler was on at the other end, the local rate-collector, a man whose whole life was one of infinite patience and guile. Off his first ball the massive Cambridge Blue was easily stumped, having executed a movement that aroused the professional admiration of the Ancient who was leaning upon his scythe. Donald was puzzled that so famous a player should play so execrable a stroke until it transpired, later on, that a wrong impression had been created and that the portentous Boone had gained his Blue at Cambridge for rowing and not for cricket. Ten runs for three wickets and one man hurt.

The next player was a singular young man. He was small and quiet, and he wore perfectly creased white flannels, white silk socks, a pale-pink shirt and a white cap. On the way down in the char-à-banc he had taken little part in the conversation and even less in the beer-drinking. There was a retiring modesty about him

that made him conspicuous in that
cricket eleven, and there was a
gentleness, an almost finicky gentleness
about his movement which hardly
seemed virile and athletic. He looked as
if a fast ball would knock the bat out
of his hands. Donald asked
someone what his name was,
and was astonished to learn
that he was the famous
novelist, Robert Southcott
himself. Just as this
celebrity, holding his bat as
delicately as if it was a flute
or a fan, was picking his
way through the daisies and
thistledown towards the wicket, Mr

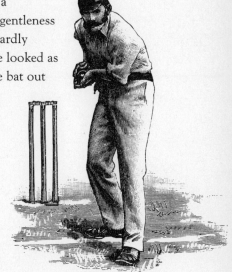

Hodge rushed anxiously, tankard in hand, from the Three
Horseshoes and bellowed in a most unpoetical voice: 'Play
carefully, Bobby. Keep your end up. Runs don't matter.'

'Very well, Bill,' replied Mr Southcott sedately. Donald was
interested by this little exchange. It was the Team Spirit at work –
the captain instructing his man to play a type of game that was
demanded by the state of the team's fortunes, and the individual
loyally suppressing his instincts to play a different type of game.

Mr Southcott took guard modestly, glanced furtively round the
field as if it was an impertinence to suggest that he would survive
long enough to make a study of the fieldsmen's positions
worthwhile, and hit the rate-collector's first ball over the Three
Horseshoes into a hay-field. The ball was retrieved by a mob of
screaming urchins, handed back to the rate-collector, who scratched
his head and then bowled his fast yorker, which Mr Southcott hit
into the saloon bar of the Shoes, giving Mr Harcourt such a fright
that he required several pints before he fully recovered his nerve.

The next ball was very slow and crafty, endowed as it was with every iota of fingerspin and brain-power which a long-service rate-collector could muster. In addition, it was delivered at the extreme end of the crease so as to secure a background of dark laurels instead of a dazzling white screen, and it swung a little in the air; a few moments later the urchins, by this time delirious with ecstasy, were fishing it out of the squire's trout stream with a bamboo pole and an old bucket.

The rate-collector was bewildered. He had never known such a travesty of the game. It was not cricket. It was slogging; it was wild, unscientific bashing; and furthermore, his reputation was in grave danger. The instalments would be harder than ever to collect, and heaven knew they were hard enough to collect as it was, what with bad times and all. His three famous deliveries had been treated with contempt – the leg-break, the fast yorker, and the slow, swinging off-break out of the laurel bushes. What on earth was he to try now? Another six and he would be laughed out of the parish. Fortunately the village umpire came out of a trance of consternation to the rescue. Thirty-eight years of umpiring for the Fordenden Cricket Club had taught him a thing or two and he called 'Over' firmly and marched off to square-leg. The rate-collector was glad to give way to a Free Forester, who had been specially imported for this match. He was only a moderate bowler, but it was felt that it was worth while giving him a trial, if only for the sake of the scarf round his waist and his cap. At the other end the fast bowler pounded away grimly until an unfortunate incident occurred. Mr Southcott had been treating with apologetic contempt those of his deliveries which came within reach, and the blacksmith's temper had been rising for some time. An urchin shouted, 'Take him orf!' and the other urchins, for whom Mr Southcott was by now a firmly established deity, had screamed with delight. The captain had held one or two ominous consultations with the wicketkeeper and other advisers, and the blacksmith knew that his dismissal was at hand unless he produced a supreme effort.

It was the last ball of the over. He halted at the wicket before going back for his run, glared at Mr Harcourt, who had been driven out to umpire by his colleagues – greatly to the regret of Mr Bason, the landlord of the Shoes – glared at Mr Southcott, took another reef in his belt, shook out another inch in his braces, spat on his hand, swung his arm three or four times in a meditative sort of way, grasped the ball tightly in his colossal palm, and then turned smartly about and marched off like a Pomeranian grenadier and vanished over the brow of the hill. Mr Southcott, during these proceedings, leant elegantly upon his bat and admired the view. At last, after a long stillness, the ground shook, the grasses waved violently, small birds arose with shrill clamours, a loud puffing sound alarmed the butterflies, and the blacksmith, looking more like Venus Anadyomene than ever, came thundering over the crest. The world held its breath. Among the spectators conversation was suddenly hushed. Even the urchins, understanding somehow that they were assisting at a crisis in affairs, were silent for a moment as the mighty figure swept up to the crease. It was the charge of Von Bredow's Dragoons at Gravelotte all over again.

But alas for human ambitions! Mr Harcourt, swaying slightly from leg to leg, had understood the menacing glare of the bowler, had marked the preparation for a titanic effort, and – for he was not a poet for nothing – knew exactly what was going on. And Mr Harcourt sober had a very pleasant sense of humour, but Mr Harcourt rather drunk was a perfect demon of impishness. Sober, he occasionally resisted a temptation to try to be funny. Rather drunk, never. As the giant whirlwind of volcanic energy rushed past him to the crease, Mr Harcourt, quivering with excitement and internal laughter, and wobbling uncertainly upon his pins, took a deep breath and bellowed, 'No ball!'

It was too late for the unfortunate bowler to stop himself. The ball flew out of his hand like a bullet and hit third-slip, who was not looking, full pitch on the knee-cap. With a yell of agony third-slip began hopping about like a stork until he tripped over a tussock of grass and fell on his face in a bed of nettles, from which he sprang up again with another drum-splitting yell. The blacksmith himself was flung forward by his own irresistible momentum, startled out of his wits by Mr Harcourt's bellow in his ear, and thrown off his balance by his desperate effort to prevent himself from delivering the ball, and the result was that his gigantic feet got mixed up among each other and he fell heavily in the centre of the wicket, knocking up a cloud of dust and dandelion-seed and twisting his ankle. Rooks by the hundred arose in protest from the vicarage cedars. The urchins howled like intoxicated banshees. The gaffers gaped. Mr Southcott gazed modestly at the ground. Mr Harcourt gazed at the heavens. Mr Harcourt did not think the world had ever been, or could ever be again, quite such a capital place, even though he had laughed internally so much that he had got hiccups.

Mr Hodge, emerging at that moment from the Three Horseshoes, surveyed the scene and then the scoreboard with an imperial air. Then he roared in the same rustic voice as before, 'You needn't play safe any more, Bob. Play your own game.'

'Thank you, Bill,' replied Mr Southcott as sedately as ever, and, on the resumption of the game, he fell into a kind of cricketing trance, defending his wicket skilfully from straight balls, ignoring crooked ones, and scoring one more run in a quarter of an hour before he inadvertently allowed, for the first time during his innings, a ball to strike his person.

'Out!' shrieked the venerable umpire before anyone had time to appeal.

The score at this point was 69 for six, last man 52.

From CRICKET COUNTRY

BY EDMUND BLUNDEN (1944)

Edmund Charles Blunden (1896–1974) was a poet, critic, scholar and man of letters whose work is known for its knowledgeable expression of rural life. This exquisite extract from his book *Cricket Country* sums up perfectly not only the game of cricket but also the atmosphere that can be found only on a summer's day in the English countryside.

* * *

THE NATIVE HEATH

BESIDE THAT SMALL ROUND POND WHICH IS ALMOST KEPT A SECRET by the massed spears of reeds rank upon rank, and beside the casual thistle-topped track which leads to an outpost farm in a kind of Netherlandish country of dikes and pollards and people working on stilts, nobody would expect to see a game of cricket played. Perhaps none ever is now. The house hard by with roofs like cliffs is in the possession of strangers, and the woods which once grew primroses enough for all the children for miles to gather and then no lack, scarcely know the flower. But in the thistly field by the pond I can remember more than one game of cricket – I speak of almost forty years ago – as an annual event which has remained in my mind much as though I had been present at some Elizabethan feast of sheep-shearers or haymakers. These old-fashioned games, which nothing of Elizabethan colour or music befriended, happened once a year, well before the general season of cricket began, and without any selection committees or posted notices. The word would go round among the boys that, however marvellous it sounded while spring was still doubtfully contesting 'unmatured green vallies cold', the match in the meadow by the pond would be played on the approaching holiday.

So on the day we went. 'Way up, Noble.' 'What cheer, Goog.' There was no question of choosing the players, or eleven a side. Those who came, played. They were of all sizes, little chaps and big; in all costumes, some in loose black leggings, some with trousers tied below the knee with coconut twine; and no particular sides were picked up. So long as someone was bowling, someone batting, the rest fielding out (with varying enthusiasm), and everybody umpiring, the match was always a success. It faded away without the strife of aggregates. The players were chiefly unfamiliar faces to me, for this field lay at the end of our sprawling parish, and the sportsmen came together from secluded cottages far down lanes bordering the orchards and shaws and hop-gardens thereabouts. What continued to keep me thinking was by no means the performance with bat and ball, a whiskery old ball, but the odd spontaneity of the whole assembly, once a year; and I observed that the young men, and one or two watch-chained elders, who then appeared as cricketers, did not for the most part make another appearance in this line of business when summer offered full chances. Indeed, even to my childish eye, they cut rather awkward figures in such appearances. What made them risk it, this once a year? What old tradition of crowded games and dances had dwindled into this pathetic little outing?

The thing might have stayed in my thoughts just as an isolated antiquarian trifle; yet, when time had carried me beyond that extreme boundary of my old home, making things once habitual claim the right of the peculiar and significant, I was more and more impressed by the depth of the cricket tradition in that part of England. It arose like a ghost out of the ground, haunting this or that stretch of short grass or pathway side, luring us to it without question or anything but willing hearts. On occasion (in the true ghost way) the spirit was absent, and though the fine evening would seem the most gloriously suitable for the game, nobody turned up.

Probably garden or farm jobs prevailed. These intervals did no harm to the next occasions when once more plenty of us came along to the unmarked place of play, and kept up an eager contest till the livelong daylight had failed and there was only glimmer enough for jests and pranks. I could draw a map of the several cricket pitches which nature and custom got ready for us, between the immemorial ring of trees by the weir where the past had seen celebrated cricketers flourish, and the mill-pool two miles east, by the banks of which pleasant-voiced Mrs Bellamy used to bowl a brilliantly varnished bouncing ball with pictures on it at her young family and their friends. It would be a map of something more than a child's play, if there is much more in human life than that.

Digressions may multiply in these pages, and this point may be almost too early for one; but as I think of these games, coming and going like wild flowers, a short speech from one of my first companions is distinct in my hearing. It will be a clearer comment than anything of my own. The cottage gardeners' flower-show of every summer was regularly the occasion for a game among the boys of the National School, who pitched their brass-topped stumps excitedly in the corner of the flaring meadow – the roundabouts would do later in the day, *and* the coconuts. My father joined in, and accordingly the cricket gained dignity and, for an hour or so, was as monotonous to us as a Test Match. There he stood at the wicket on one afternoon never to be forgotten – a batsman of some calibre, a grown-up, a large batsman. Behind the other wicket Will Bellamy, who was a sturdy boy, with a mighty serious expression, clutching the ball in one hand and clenching the other, prepared to bowl at the giant. The first or second time he tried, the ball sailed over an oak tree in the next meadow, aromatic with swathes of new-mown hay. Once or twice more the ball flew afar as the magician smote. But then, not quite losing hope, Will whirled his arm over again, the bat flashed and the wicket fell! I am not sure that the game was allowed to continue after this climax; but I recollect (when time had travelled on) walking past the empty field under the starry arch of a December night with Will, who, being about twelve years of age, crowned a solemn conversation with the following pronouncement: 'I think that was the Best Ball I ever Bowled *in my life.*'

The tradition of the game in our valley of the orchards maintaining its easy succession year upon year, suddenly grew clearer to me a long time afterwards on an evening when, sitting at a window overlooking the green and listening to the shouts of 'Throw in' caused by the slashing batsmanship of a black-haired girl there, I glanced into the newly bought volume of letters of an eighteenth-century poet. The popular author of *The Minstrel* (as I then discovered) stayed now and then in a mood of Arcadian fondness and the picturesque, in the village adjoining ours. He was a Scot, but was not unkind to our southern manners, and he did not disdain to record in his reports to the philosophers at home a cricket match of yearly consequence played, with lots of beer and cheerfulness, in a field opposite the village church. There, amid the long grass, matches were still being played until the first World War, and may yet be after the second, though Sports Clubs perhaps do not quite pass as direct heirs of the sons of the village, in sight of their friend and enemy the 'stubborn glebe,' taking off their jackets as if to assail it once again – but this time for a diversion.

Long live diversion! Among all the charming things that I have had the luck to meet with in town and country, the unofficial, undeveloped game will not swiftly lose my love, even though I may not now or ever delve out my reason for loving it. Yet many others besides must feel a lightening of all that was a burden when all of a sudden the children, punctual as the swallow or the bluebell, and inquiring no more than those into the theory of their revivals, come out with the sport of the season. Wanton wits inform me that these seasons of games are directed by nothing more mysterious than business ingenuity; but I cannot see that at the present hour when the little boys are lashing far from new tops,

and not less fascinated than in better times, when new tops were so numerous. Marbles, tops of various shape and various function – the window-breaker never was so bad as his name, the peg-top always looked more sinister to me – had-you-last, tipcat or nipcat, rounders, skipping, hopscotch, high-cockalorum, wagon and horses, show-your-light, hide-ee-up, hoops, sheep and wolf and a host of other sports besides cricket with a rag ball, come kindly out of the past at childhood's call. When it is decided that the new one must come, the old goes away in a twinkling into the strange country where it sleeps. Some of these games, you may tell me, are under suspicion of having gone for ever,

'Where's Troy, and where's the Maypole in the Strand?'

Modernity does not refrain from the toys of children: games in the end must die like parts of Homer and Shakespeare, or be modified as much as the cricket bat of to-day, spliced and complex-handled, is altered from the curved cudgel of the same name in the days of George the Third. Modification is a deity worth a canto of some new poet's imagining. When we reflect that, as a masterly philologer was reminding me lately, 'a newt' and 'an eft' are the same word, we may conclude that the unusual appearance of a thing does not constitute a new thing. Because we did not lately see a game we knew, a toy we smiled at in the village street or in Mariners' Court, we need not at once turn to composing elegies for its being at last irrecoverably sent away from the world. The game may, like baseball, subject to this modification, rise afresh in a shape of rapid tremendous power, conquering continents. Or it may steal in among its old company very much as it was, a *revenant* which frightens nobody and in action is as courteous and acceptable as the weather around its glittering eyes and clapping hands.

I sometimes hear it proposed that cricket, the ever changeful, changeless game which some even among the English view as the prime English eccentricity, is a something to which, for thorough appreciation, a man must have been bred from the cradle or about there. If this is the truth, I qualify; for in our village and our county the game was so native, so constant, so beloved without fuss that it came to me as the air I breathed and the morning and evening. Time has altered me, though some who know me will not admit it in this connection; but there were many of us whose childhood was moulded in the same way. Some boys of course did not enjoy cricket, and we wondered at them, and thought them unsocial. Some of the older people reproved the zealous as 'cricket-mad,' but we heard that for all their growlings they were once players – indeed it came out that Mr J. who frowned and even cast imprecations on the noise of our playground game, was a collector of books on cricket. Others never took a seat on the boundary of the village ground, who all the same did not miss a football match. Still, it may be held that cricket lay much as Wordsworth's heaven about boys like me in our infancy, in act and word colouring our minds – and who was I to quarrel with the world into which I had come? There perpetually you had the cherry orchard, there the grammar school, there the dairy farm, the brewery, the wharf, the church, the cricket field – and I was convinced, if convincing was required, that God had been doing his best in all these arrangements.

Those were the days of clergymen cricketers. Our own vicar was the greatest example of these whom I ever saw. I have certainly encountered others whose careers were longer – one, for example, who delivered at me the most agitating underhand bowling at the age of seventy, and duly added me to his monotonous list of victims. But the impression this ancient lobster made was in every way narrower. It astonished me to watch the vicar on Sundays in summer, when morning and evening for a few hours he became the priest and bore the sway and dignity, imparted the light and consolation of a sound divine. I secretly marvelled that this should be the same man who yesterday kept wicket and slaughtered the over-pitched ball with such absolute, single devotion. It was a similar though a lowlier Sabbath mystery in the case of some of the choirmen, who had divested themselves, it seemed, not only of their cricket boots and pads but also of their principal object in life – for that one day of the week. But I had my suspicions.

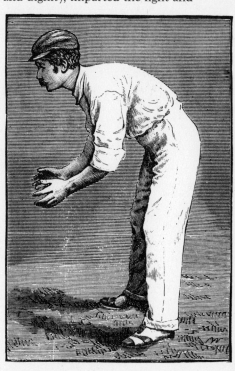

In the vestry, during the crowded expectant moments before we marched forth singing our hymn, or 'Lead me, Lord' to our choir seats, I observed that the vicar with a rich smile would sometimes hold a whispered conversation apart with one or two of his cricketers. It might have been, of course, enlightenment on a theological nicety, or a thought on church music, but I did get the

impression that the Sunday paper had not been safely received at
the Vicarage before the vicar left, and that some such inquiry as
'How many did Kent make altogether?' or 'Did the Australians put
us in, then?' was made and answered. (News in those days did not
come before its time.) Or it might be something nearer home: 'That
fellow you ran out seemed pretty miserable about something,
Judd.' – 'Yes, sir, he told the scorer that you had told him to go –
"safe run there, my boy."' – 'Well, did I?' stroking a smooth chin as
if in a deep consideration.

The epitaph of the vicar now glimmers upon the nave of the
church which he, for so many years, served with ability, affection
and religion. It is a just tribute to his worth as a parish priest,
though no short inscription could intimate that handsome
presence (yielding a touch of the Falstaffian peculiarly blended
with the aristocratic) or renew the strong and stirring notes of that
voice. 'When the wicked man turneth away from his wickedness…'
'Let your light so shine before men' (how welcome he made the
very offertory!) – monitions like these echo on for me still in his
intonation, and even as a child I determined that, as *he* had drawn
my attention to them, I ought to do something about them. He, if
any one in the land, had authority. The tablet to his memory
cannot re-create the light of his countenance, though it gives his
dates; and in the opinion of some who knew him it lacks
something else, which was not beyond its powers or its proper
nature. The centuries will read it (if the bombs go on missing it, as
a scattering of them did one startling summer night) never guessing
that the subject was for many summers the pattern of cricket
enthusiasm, the incumbent of the village ground. And in that era
that was something.

From SECOND INNINGS

BY NEVILLE CARDUS (1950)

Sir Neville Cardus (1889–1975) was perhaps the most famous
cricket writer of them all. In 1919 he became cricket correspondent
for the *Manchester Guardian* and whilst there revolutionized writing
on the game, becoming particularly well known for his articles on
Lancashire heroes of the day. He was awarded a CBE in 1964 and
was knighted in 1967 for services to cricket and music writing.

* * *

I CANNOT REMEMBER HOW I BECAME INTERESTED IN THE GAME OF
cricket. There were no games organized at the Board school
which I attended more or less irregularly, morning and afternoon,
from the age of eight to thirteen, when I joined the ranks of the
employed. These five years of my formal education were
interrupted by an illness which kept me in bed nearly a year,
suffering from what was at the time rather unscientifically known
as an abscess on the lungs. A steam kettle maintained the
temperature of my bedroom, and every morning the doctor, a
clean polished gentleman with a black coat and striped trousers
and a white border in his waistcoat, put some tubes to my chest,
and listened. I liked the smell of him, the way he would flop his
gloves into his tall hat.

The Board school did not extend its curriculum beyond the
'three Rs', a list of 'dates' in English history, and some geography
about peninsulas being nearly surrounded by water. The main thing
apparently was to awaken us to a sense of inborn sin; we were
taught Scripture every morning at nine o'clock, and the boy who
showed the faintest sign of freedom of the will was caned. It was
almost impossible to avoid some form of punishment from the

various teachers, nearly all women beyond the first flush of
maidenhood. There was a Miss Barthwick, of yellow visage, and
hair parted straight down the middle. She frequently called me out
of the class and told me to hold out my hand. Then she would
select a cane from a number of them, and 'try it' by bending it on
the desk in front of her. I was astounded that sometimes when she
passed me in the street outside school hours she would give me a
smile of kindly recognition. I could not believe that school
teachers were capable of living private lives, of enjoying
themselves, relaxing and absenting themselves from vigilance
awhile.

Once only in my life have I wished to kill anybody. I edited a
private paper, *The Boy's World*, written in an exercise-book, in
patient and beautiful copper-plate handwriting; I spent hours and
hours over this labour of love on winter nights, a hundred pages,
which I would circulate amongst my companions free of charge. I
was author of all the serial stories, under various assumed names,
emulative of Henry St John. I invented a rival to Sherlock Holmes.
His name was Dexter Deane; no detective worth his salt owned to
an ordinary Christian name such as George or Henry. I conducted
an 'Editor's Den' and occasionally followed the fashion of the
boys' journals of the period by running a competition; 'missing
words' or some such, awarding a first prize of £5 a week for life.

One day while I was surreptitiously handing round my
periodical (fresh from the press) under cover of the desks, the
teacher saw it, demanded to have it, and in front of the class she
tore it to pieces – a rather lengthy task – and then threw it into a
waste-paper basket. If the wish to murder is a capital offence, I was
then as guilty as any man that ever walked to the scaffold after
eating a hearty breakfast. Perhaps a merciful judge would have
acquitted me under the First Offenders' Act. The teacher was one
of the younger females of the staff. I remember her clearly to this
day; she wore little oval spectacles, and when I caught a glimpse of
the world through the edges of the lenses, as she stood near me,

everything was very brilliant and small.

Our games were of our own
arranging. We played cricket on the
fields adjacent to the semi-slums in
which I lived. They were not really
fields; we called them
'brickcrofts'; already the
jerry-builder was at work
upon 'greater Manchester'.
There is a narrow street
in Rusholme, my birth
district, where a row of
drab dwelling-places now
stands, unless the
Germans bombed them
out of existence; and any
summer evening some hot and
hopeless housewife cooks the evening meal on the very spot where
once we played over and over again Lancashire and Yorkshire
matches witnessed at Old Trafford, or even a Test Match. We aped
the heroes of the period. We began our games after 'tea' and went
on until total darkness. One evening I would announce that I was
Lockwood and about to bowl fast; the next evening I might change
myself to Rhodes and bowl so slowly that the ball scarcely reached
the block-hole. It all depended upon what the day's cricket scores
chanced to reveal and extol.

I must have taken very early to the game. I can clearly recall
looking at the stop-press scores in the *Manchester Evening News*,
and reading 'Tyldesley, b. Anthony, 222,' tidings of great joy from
Trent Bridge, where Lancashire were that day playing 'Notts'. The
date was round about 1900. It was certainly in this same summer
that I entered the county cricket ground of Old Trafford for the
first time, the first time of many.

More than forty years ago! Old Trafford was almost in the

country then, Stretford was a village and there was no British
Westinghouse. At the top of Warwick Road stood the Botanical
Gardens; for some reason or other, gardens devoted to botany were
supposed to serve as a means towards culture amongst the masses.
I saw William Gunn in these gardens one evening; but I don't think
he was studying botany. More than forty years ago, when a small
boy nine years and three months old first saw the dread sign
outside Old Trafford: 'The public takes its own risk of the weather.
No money returned.' A year or two later, on a Saturday in July,
1902, I hesitated outside these forbidding gates; heavy rain-clouds
darkened the sky. Then I heard a roar of agony from the crowd
within and I risked my sixpence. This was the afternoon Australia
won the rubber by three runs; I saw the collapse after MacLaren
had fallen to a catch in the deep in an attempt to get the runs
before the rain came. I think it is the truth that as Ranjitsinhji sat
on the amateurs' balcony waiting for his turn to bat on this
afternoon of agony, he carved his initials on the windowledge
without knowing what he was doing. When in his turn he had to
face Trumble and Saunders, he was marvellously and incredibly
reduced to impotence, and failed miserably. This story is old and
historical. The father of Maurice Tate came in when eight runs
were needed, and by reflex action achieved four of them, then died
the death. A year or so ago I saw and spoke to one of the few
surviving members of this nobly tragic Test match, none other
than Clem Hill, who caught out Lilley running yards and yards
after what seemed a certain four from a low skimming drive. Hill
claimed that he turned two somersaults after gripping the ball.
Also he declared that MacLaren's language was spontaneous and
empurpled.

They say it always rains at Old Trafford. But weather or
industrial gloom or what not, the frieze of Old Trafford's cricket,
the great sequence, comes back to mind as though lighted by
eternal sunshine. Hornby and Barlow, the roaring ruddy Cheshire
squire and his dour henchman. Briggs and his sad Grimaldi

grimace; the stately Albert Ward, a whole Sunday School of batsmanship in himself. MacLaren, Spooner and J. T. Tyldesley, the three most brilliant batsmen that ever opened any country's innings one after the other. Walter Brearley, who bowled fast from morning till night until his eyes were coming out of his head and his face was as red as a boiled lobster. The rich Lancashire stuff of Harry Dean, Lol Cook, who always bowled into the wind, and knew that his demand for leg-before would fall on stone-deaf ears. Richard Tyldesley, emerging from three sweaters on a cold day; Duckworth crowing like a cock. I think I was the first man he ever stumped at Old Trafford; it was a so-called friendly match, and when I missed the ball and Duckworth shrieked his appeal and swept up all the bails and the stumps, I felt as though I had been sandbagged. And there was Parkin, lovable stormy petrel, spin and high spirits; when he was in form and getting wickets every over he used to sing comic songs.

Victor Trumper scored a century before lunch at Old Trafford in the same famous three-runs Test Match of 1902. At Old Trafford, Ranjitsinhji not only ended his Test Match career but in 1896 performed there one of his most oriental conjurations against the Australian fast bowler, Ernest Jones; he glanced greased lightning from his left ear down to fine-leg for a four of a velocity rendered almost visible and luminous.

Another great Australian fast bowler – the most beautiful of them all – found his happiest hunting-ground at Old Trafford, his name McDonald, and his graceful ghost will be seen in the sunshine that falls on the next Lancashire and Yorkshire match played there. There were Makepeace and Watson, too, determined to stay in all day against Rhodes and Emmott Robinson; no boundaries before lunch, lads, on principle tha knows. Lancashire and Yorkshire, the greatest match of all, certainly the funniest. Think of it – Rhodes bowling protectively, with determination not to drop a ball anywhere within the hitting zone, bowling with all his cunning on a 'safety-first' spot to a Makepeace who would have died rather than have hit the easiest half-volley – at any rate before lunch.

Many years ago, during the calmer moments of a Lancashire v. Yorkshire match, I wrote a passage as follows: 'At three o'clock there was no place on earth where I would rather have been than at Old Trafford. Sunshine fell on the field, and the venerable pavilion stood in the summer light; white clouds sailed in the sky and the Lancashire colours, with the Red Rose, fluttered in the gentle breeze. And the crowd indulged the old humours, never growing weary of them. Grand cheers greeted a piece of dashing fielding; roars fit to split the heavens went out when Lancashire passed the Yorkshire first innings total. A golden day, a noble crowd, and the greenest grass in England! Many a Lancashire man, exiled from this blessed country, now imprisoned across the seas, was thinking yesterday of Old Trafford and saying to his heart, "Oh to be there – whoever's batting!"'

Those lines were written in August, 1926; and it is myself, as I write these lines, that am now the exiled one, far away in Australia, saying to his heart, 'Oh to be there'; and saying also, 'Greetings, Old Trafford, even if it's Lancashire that is still batting!'

From FAREWELL TO CRICKET

BY DON BRADMAN (1950)

Sir Donald Bradman (1908–2001) was not only an Australian
sporting hero but is the only Australian knighted for services to
the game of cricket. He scored 6,996 runs in 52 Test matches and
set a record with his average of 99.94 runs. 'I am quite certain,' Bill
O'Reilly – a former Test cricketer – once said that, 'he was the best
cricketer ever to walk on to a cricket ground in any part of the
whole wide world'.

* * *

ON CAPTAINCY

WHEN THE RIVAL CAPTAINS GO OUT INTO THE MIDDLE TO TOSS
in a Test Match, what are they thinking? What problems
confront them? I suppose thoughts like these constantly run through
the minds of the spectators. But do they ever ponder over the
apprenticeship these captains have served before being appointed to
such responsible positions? The actual game itself is the moment of
action. Years of thought and training have preceded it.

It was my good fortune to captain Australia in five Test series –
four against England and one against India. During that period
Australia did not lose a rubber, but I lost a great deal of sleep. Not
for a moment do I claim any special ability as a captain. I do claim
to have learnt many lessons from my experiences, all of which
emphasize the necessity of hard work and application. There is no
short cut.

At school I had virtually no opportunity. The cricket was not
competitive except on rare occasions. I did not have control of a
team, broadly speaking, until I first captained a grade side. I was

still far from confident when the task of handling a Test team came my way. My own consciousness that I was relatively inexperienced only increased my anxiety and may have caused me at first to move along strictly orthodox lines.

The first duty of a captain is to win the toss. This is pure luck, though some captains have been blessed with more than their share. I was not one of them.

In 1936 I lost the first two and won the last three.

In 1938 I lost all four.

In 1946–7 I won two and lost three.

Against India 1947–8 I won four out of five.

In England 1948 I lost four out five.

The summary shows that I won ten out of twenty-four – just less than half. A rather interesting point is that Australia did not lose one Test Match in which I won the toss.

Winning the toss is not always an advantage. The winner has to make his decision, whereas the loser is sometimes spared such an embarrassment. Sometimes the loss of the toss enables a win to be gained due to the time factor. Take a case where A bats first and makes 400. B replies with 350. A then makes 300 for five declared, and B is nine for 170 when the match ends in a draw. Team A has a margin of 180 runs to get one wicket. Assuming the reverse batting order, team A might have won comfortably by eight wickets. I am certain we won the 1948 Nottingham Test because I lost the toss. It enabled our speed bowlers to break through quickly while there was still life in the pitch.

Wickets do not always play as anticipated. At Lord's in 1948 I won the toss and decided to bat, fortified by the groundsman's forecast 'slow and easy'. It turned out to be a real 'green top' and we struggled very hard to survive.

Unfortunately for a captain the spotlight of publicity beats very fiercely upon his every move. What he should or should not do is chronicled in advance by experienced and inexperienced critics. They have no responsibility. The skipper's decisions are minutely analysed, and the verdict given in the light of after events. There lies the big difference. A captain must make every decision *before* he knows what its effect will be, and he must carry the full responsibility, not of whether his decision will be right or wrong but whether it brings success. The margin between success or failure can be so slender.

Cast your mind back to Leeds in 1926. Arthur Carr, having won the toss for England, sent Australia in to bat. Bardsley was caught first ball. Off the fifth ball Carr himself had the mortification of dropping Macartney, who showed his appreciation by making a century before lunch. Had Carr held that catch his decision might have been hailed as a master-stroke – instead he was torn to shreds. The captain's decision may be perfectly correct according to all available information – one mistake and he is undone.

Sometimes personal considerations intrude. Many a captain has sacrificed his own wicket to the detriment of his side because he feared the stigma of not attempting to set an example to his men. It is all very well to be gallant and heroic, but the captain's job embodies the welfare of the team, and if his own personal success is an integral part of victory, he should act accordingly. On several occasions I was compelled to rearrange our batting order as a matter of tactics because of the state of the wicket. It almost inevitably succeeded. Some were unkind enough to suggest that my purpose was to avoid batting on a wet wicket. Of course it was; but only because such avoidance was necessary in the interests of the team.

Cricket fields behave in a variety of ways after rain. The man never lived whose judgement was infallible. Not the least difficulty is to decide how long a wicket will remain bad. Under Australian conditions sufficient rain on a hard wicket, followed by hot sun, will generally produce a glue pot. Some are worse than others. But will it remain sticky for an hour or all day? One cannot tell. In 1936–7, against Allen's team, we worked like beavers to try and get quick wickets. Then I found the pitch was drying more slowly than anticipated and had to tell my bowlers not to get England out.

The question of field placing is a captain's natural responsibility, though he will, if wise, work in harmony with his bowlers. Decisions might have to be taken occasionally on matters where the captain's judgement must prevail over that of his men. For instance, I often had difficulty with slip fieldsmen who insisted on standing too deep. From my side view at cover, I thought the ball would not carry to them. They, in turn, said if they stood closer they would not be able to hold a catch. My reply was, 'If the ball doesn't reach you, you can't catch it. Better to drop a catch than not be in a position to attempt it.' I was always very particular about the position of fieldsmen. I might even have been called fussy. But it is important. One might just as well miss a catch by ten feet as three inches, and if a captain anticipates the possibility of a catch going in a certain place it is his job to put the fieldsmen *exactly* in that spot – not somewhere near it. This applies more forcibly to positions near the wicket.

A constant problem is the task of deciding the right moment to make a bowling change. Your fast bowler is getting wickets but tiring rapidly. Shall he be used right up in the hope of achieving quick results or shall he be rested for a later effort? Perhaps a bowler is doing well when a batsman comes in who is renowned for his weakness against some other bowler. Should a change be made at once? These are typical problems which cannot be decided in advance. The best captain is the man who can get the best out of his men and achieve results with a poor combination.

For instance, there was no skill shown by Armstrong in opening the bowling with Gregory and McDonald. To follow them was such an array as Hendry (medium pace), Macartney (slow left-hand), Mailey and Armstrong (slow right-hand). It was a tailor-made combination. What a difference to some of the later teams when the openers were really only medium-pace change bowlers!

Generally speaking, it seems that a batsman is a better type for captain than a bowler. He is spared the unfortunate choice of whether to overbowl himself or not. Wasn't it George Giffen who acceded to the crowd's entreaties to 'take yourself off' by going on the other end? Also, I think the captain should be a player whose place in the team is indisputable. If a skipper has need to worry about his own position, it must detract from his ability to make untrammelled decisions.

I always liked playing under a captain who was firm but kindly. There is no joy in playing under a man who lets you wander round the field where you will, or who will hesitate when necessary to tell you what is required of you. I think players react much better to the leader who sets them a high target. Complete cricketers should

constantly be seeking ways of assisting their captain. It is a fundamental duty so to do. A variety of temperaments does not always enable this perfection to be attained.

Sometimes a conflict may arise between the desire to please the public and the need to adopt an unattractive or unpopular policy. It can be most disconcerting if the public is clamouring for action and the captain feels it necessary to instruct his men to 'dig in'. Strong-minded players will often succumb to these external influences. If both captains are bent upon making the play attractive, there is little difficulty in providing entertaining cricket. Should one captain depart from this attitude, the game can be ruined as a spectacle. More than once I was criticized for unimaginative tactics when in fact I was only combating those of my opponents. I did not believe in initiating slow play, and only resorted to it in cases of necessity.

One thing all captains (and players) should do is to make themselves conversant with the rules governing the game. Apart from the value to be so gained, they are a fascinating study.

This has been a sketchy outline of some captaincy problems. They are very real. A great many of them on the field are obvious. Off the field they are not so obvious but perhaps more onerous. If any young player aspires to the leadership of an Australian eleven, let him do so only if imbued with the idea of service. It isn't always pleasant trying to please 50,000 spectators, fifty journalists and ten other players. Sometimes I think the public would do well to ponder that captains are normal, sensitive human beings, striving so hard to do the right thing. They are not a race apart. Public support is a great tonic when the going is hard.

From BRIGHTLY FADES THE DON

BY J. H. FINGLETON (1949)

John Henry Fingleton (1908–1981) was a fine opening batsman for
Australia, if not quite in the same league as Don Bradman, Bill
Ponsford or Bill Woodfull. A journalist by profession, he wrote
regularly while playing. The following piece is a mellow portrait of
the cricketing legend, Harold Larwood, who was sometimes known
as the 'Demon Bowler' or the 'Silent Killer' owing to his
inestimable bowling skills..

* * *

RETREAT FROM BOWLING GLORY

IT WAS IN A SIDE STREET IN BLACKPOOL THAT WE FOUND HIM.
George Duckworth, one of his best friends in his playing days,
knew the way. 'It is a neat little mixed shop,' said George, 'but you
won't find his name on it.' And we didn't, which was strange,
because in his day his name was possibly even as famous as
Bradman's, but he had not only finished with all that. He had not
the slightest wish to be reminded of it.

His eldest daughter saw us first. She recognized George and
gave him a great welcome, smiling broadly and motioning towards
the back of the house. And there in a homely room, its walls
festooned with photographs of some of the most stirring times
known to the game of cricket, he gave me a quiet but warm
welcome. He recognized me immediately, though I was the first
Australian cricketer he had met since those stormy days of 1932–3,
when his name was sprawled across the columns of newspapers in
much the same manner as he sprawled his victims across the
cricket field, but in 1948 he was much thinner. Walking behind

him, one would never guess that here was the greatest fast bowler of the modern age; the possessor, in his time, of as lovely a bowling action as the game has ever known. But his face, though thinner, had not changed much. He was still the same Harold Larwood.

The conversation, for a time, was circumspect. Not only was I one of the 'enemy' of 1932–3 but I was a newspaperman, and Larwood had memories of how he had been publicized over the years by the stunting gentry of my profession. Then, in addition, he wanted to bury the dead. You saw that, clearly, in his refusal to have his name shown in the slightest manner over his shop. Dozens of former cricketers throughout the world, whose claim to fame could not compare with his, have capitalized their glory by having their names over balls or bats, by having it in books, by having it up in big letters outside their places of business, but not in the slightest manner, and certainly not by having his name blazoned to the outside world, did Harold Larwood wish to recapture the past. He wanted only to forget it, and so his business, to all appearance, was no different to thousands of similar businesses throughout England that are run by the Joneses, the Browns, Williamses and Smiths.

It was a pinch of snuff, so to speak, that broke the ice. He took out his box and offered it to me. I declined. Not so George Duckworth. 'Aay, laad,' said George, taking a copious pinch. He placed it on the back of his hand, slapped it with the other, sniffed simultaneously and forthwith began to sneeze so vigorously that tears ran from his eyes. Larwood smiled and took his with the air of a man long accustomed to the art.

'You know,' he said to me, 'I always had snuff in my pocket when I was bowling. I often used to take a pinch of it on the field in Australia. It used to freshen me up. And it's much better for you than cigarettes.

An eminent medical authority in the last century, Dr Gordon Hake, would have approved of that. 'Snuff,' wrote Dr Hake to a critic of his habit, 'not only wakes up that torpor so prevalent between the nose and the brain, making the wings of an idea uncurl like those of a new-born butterfly, but while others sneeze and run at the eyes my schneiderian membrane is impervious to the weather or, to be explicit, I never take a cold in the head.' Soon after the introduction of snuff into Britain in the eighteenth century, the *Gentlewoman's Companion*, noble production, was advising its gentle readers whose sight was failing to use the right sort of Portugal snuff 'whereby many eminent people had cured themselves so that they could read without spectacles after having used them for many years'.

As Larwood was snuffing, I thought his Australian opponents might have been a little better off in 1932–3 had somebody got his box away from him. He might not have sighted his target or his victim so readily, but here at Blackpool, in 1948, it cleared the atmosphere, and when, at long last, George got his schneiderian membrane to behave, the three of us fell to discussing the old days in a reminiscent manner. There was no bitterness. I had taken many on the ribs from Larwood and Voce, in those bodyline days, but all that was forgotten as we recalled the players of those days and the many incidents – for incidents happened in the bodyline series every other minute.

One has not to talk long with Larwood to realize that he is still embittered over those days. I don't think it is with the Australians, but rather with those English officials who were glad to have him and use him before bodyline became ostracized, and then, conveniently, put him aside. He finds that impossible to forgive. Like the prodigal son, he would have been welcomed home by the MCC in 1935 and had all forgiven, but Larwood is a man of strong beliefs. To satisfy all and sundry, the MCC wished Larwood to apologize to them. Had he done that, like Voce, he would have been chosen again for the Australian tour of 1936–7, but Larwood could not see that he had anything to apologize over, and so he remained adamant and went out of the game under a cloud.

He did not say so, but I gathered he considered himself badly ~ated, and many who know the story of those bodyline days will gree with him. With us, he recalled only the happy memories of the most distressing tour in cricket history, though when we talked of Bradman I detected again the same old glint of battle I had seen in his eye when I had faced up to him as a batsman.

'When I bowled against Bradman,' he said, 'I always thought he was out to show me up as the worst fast bowler in the world. Well, I took the view that I should try and show him up as the worst batsman. But, laad, he was a good 'un.'

We fell to looking through his photograph albums and the reminiscences among the three of us came thick and fast. His eldest daughter (and Larwood has five beautiful daughters, the youngest between our legs on the floor) had just begun to take an interest in cricket and, only a few days before, Larwood had got out his souvenirs to show her, and they included numerous balls with silver rings about them describing how in many places he had performed great bowling feats.

Larwood made some pretty shrewd observations about batsmen. He reeled off the names of famous batsmen who, he considered, couldn't play the hook stroke and were thus at a disadvantage against him. The cricket world would be amazed if I repeated the men he named, but, like Keith Miller, the Australian, he considered himself fully entitled to prove their weaknesses with bouncers. But how the wheel has now turned full circle! Here, in 1948, under Bradman, the Australians exploited the bouncers to the full (though without the packed leg-field of Jardine), and members of the Nottingham County Committee, the same committee which was forced to apologize to Woodfull and his team in 1934 because Voce had bowled bumpers, now admonished its own spectators for barracking against Australian bumpers. The cricket world, surely, is as crazy and as inconsistent as the outside one.

It was with difficulty that we induced Larwood to come with us

to a cricket game for charity which we were playing on the
Blackpool ground. He compromised to the extent of promising to
come down after afternoon tea. He had not seen either the 1934 or
1938 Australian teams in action. He had not seen his C.-in-C.,
Douglas Jardine, since Jardine had played in his benefit game in
1935. He had not seen this present Australian team in action,
though he had a hankering to see Lindwall bowl. He could not
remember the last time he had seen a game on his old home
ground, Trent Bridge. Cricket had lost all its appeal for Larwood.

He came to the charity game, forced into it, we thought, by his
family, who liked to see him with old associates. He told me a story
I loved. It was about Sir Pelham Warner and myself and concerned
the bodyline tour. It happened during the Adelaide game, where
feeling was tremendously high, and where Woodfull used strong
words to Warner over the tactics of the M.C.C. team. That story
ran quickly to the Press, and Sir Pelham, jumping to conclusions
because I was a pressman, wrongly blamed me for the breach of
ethics.

'As we were going out to field in your second innings,' said
Larwood, 'Sir Pelham said to me, "Larwood, I will give you a
pound if you bowl Fingleton out quickly." If you remember, I did,
and when I came off the field Sir Pelham was waiting there at the
door with a pound note in his hand.'

I will never forget that ball. It was the best ever bowled to me
in cricket. At Larwood's top speed, it changed course in the air
from leg and, continuing on that course, pitched about the leg and
middle stump and took the off-bail. It was absolutely unplayable. A
batsman never minds being dismissed by a good ball, even for
nothing, as I was that day.

'Ah, well,' said Larwood, 'those days are gone for ever, but
here's a pound note. Let's go and have a drink and we will say it is
on Sir Pelham.'

There were times, during the Australian tour of bodyline, when
Larwood thought the game not worth the candle. He knew abuse.

The tumult was overpowering, the work of fast bowling hard. He has a very sensitive side to his nature and often wondered whether it was worth it, but then he allowed his mind to revert to his coal-mining days before he played cricket, and that was sufficient. Strangely, on that tour, his stomach revolted against food. He found that beer, with his occasional pinch of snuff on the field, gave him all the sting he wanted. From the Australian viewpoint, it gave him more than enough, but he will always be remembered in Australia, tactics of that MCC side apart, as the Prince of Bowlers.

It was a coincidence that very day that Larwood should have received from Australia a long letter from a youth on the art of bowling. It was an interesting letter, asking for advice. It was fitting, even though this lad had never seen Larwood bowl, that he should have written to such a one for advice, though I smiled to myself as I read this delightful piece of youthful folly. 'Do you think, Mr Larwood,' wrote this ardent theorist, 'that you might have been a better fast bowler if you had begun the swing of your right arm from lower down?' As if any Australian would have wanted Larwood to be better than he was. But perhaps the oddest thing of all about this letter was that it came from Bowral, home town of Bradman. How quaint if Bowral, through Bradman's greatest antagonist on the field, should produce another Larwood!

When we parted we had extracted from him almost a half-promise that he would come to Old Trafford and see and meet the Australians. He wanted to meet O'Reilly; he wanted to see Lindwall particularly, but Larwood never came. I think the inside of an English first-class ground contained too many sad memories for him. He deserved better of the game; he deserved better, particularly, of English cricket, because, in tactics, he was only a cog in a wheel. He was, for a certainty, the only bowler who ever quelled Bradman; the only bowler who made Bradman lose his poise and balance, departing from his set path of easeful centuries into flurried and agitated movements.

I left Blackpool glad that I had seen Larwood, and I think that he, for his part, was pleased again to meet an Australian cricketer, the first since the field of battle in 1932–3. There is something tragic about his finish in cricket and the fact that he wishes to have no ties with the game at all now. It is interesting, too, to look back to those days of 1932–3 and reflect what time has done for the central figures, Bradman and Larwood. The game has been over-kind to one, unkind to the other; but that has ever been the way of cricket. It is a game, mostly, for batsmen, and I thought of all this as I left Larwood on the note, of all things, of migration. He thinks hard these days of bringing his lovely family of five daughters to settle in a country which once flamed from end to end over his bowling. That, surely, must be the oddest thought of all – Larwood settled in Australia! But he would be doubly welcome. Australia has never held anything against Larwood.

HILL CRICKET

BY LAURIE LEE (1980)

Laurie Lee (1914–1997) was an English poet and prose writer, best known for his 1959 novel, *Cider with Rosie*, which became an instant classic, recalling as it did the simplicity and innocence of rural English life. The following piece, which first appeared in the August 1980 issue of *Wisden Cricket Monthly*, is a wonderful story about a visit Lee made to Sydney to watch a cricket match during which he gets inadvertently 'blooded'.

* * *

I COME FROM A COUNTRY OF HILL-CRICKET, WHERE FOR DECADES THE village players have been great toilers on the slopes and have developed a whole range of off-the-level techniques. Indeed, in those steep valleys running away through the Cotswold escarpment it was well-nigh impossible to find a level space for a wicket, and the most we could hope for, when we were boys, was some well-trodden goat-path winding among the tussocks.

One of the most unbalanced, yet beautiful, of cricket fields in my local district is the one that stands high on its hill above the village of Sheepscombe. Its general contour is that of a pony's back, with head held erect – the pavilion built somewhere between the ears, then the pitch itself starting halfway down the neck, levelling off for a bit along the saddle then plunging down the hind-quarters and away to the boundary. A straight drive from one end runs slap into the hill and, after trickling for a few yards, stops dead; while from the other end it soars out and disappears over the brow of the hill, till the ball is returned by some passing cowman.

A lasting memory of this ground is of sitting on the pavilion porch and watching Frank Mansell – Sheepscombe's demon bowler

– come racing up the hill to deliver. At first only outfield was
visible, then you'd see the top of Frank's cap, then his flushed face
and great heaving shoulders, till gradually, like a galleon, he'd come
billowing into view and loose his fast one like a shot from a
cannon.

Some time during the late twenties I bicycled from our hills
down into Cheltenham to see Gloucestershire play the visiting
Australians. I remember Arthur Mailey and others in their huge
cloth caps – strange bottle-faced men from the other side of the
world who laughed sharply and spoke a kind of scrambled
Cockney. Watching the fierceness of their game on that green
English ground, I began to speculate about the country they came
from, and how they played cricket in their own home towns, and
what their pitches were like 15,000 miles down through the bulk of
the world. Later, I began to hear tales of 'The Hill' at Sydney, and
what with hills being so much a part of our local game, I started to
wonder about this too. One day, I swore, I'd go there and see them
at it. I'd sit on The Hill at Sydney and feel at home.

A few years ago I arranged this at last while staying with my
brother, who lives near the cricket ground at Sydney. It was
Christmas-summer, the time of a Test series against New Zealand,
and we dressed up one afternoon and went to see the game. Our
destination, it seemed, was the Members' Pavilion, but I asked for
The Hill instead. This was reluctantly agreed to, and together with
another friend – one of the many sons of an ex-Archbishop of
Canterbury – we picked our way carefully towards that legendary
place.

It was a bright hot day, with tiny clouds in the sky and a keen
air smelling of freshly picked oysters. This was soon enriched by
the smell of freshly pricked beer-cans as several thousand cricket-
watchers settled down to the game. They were a striking lot, many
half-naked, with thin wiry legs supporting huge muscled torsos.
Each wore round his middle, like a Lonsdale belt, the sacred pot of
the dedicated beer-drinker. And almost everyone had beside him,

to accompany the afternoon's play, several dozen beer cans or bottles packed in great portable ice-boxes. As one for whom a normal afternoon at Lord's might have absorbed at most a couple of long-held pints, the sight and quantity of each man's supply struck me as another dimension of cricket altogether.

New Zealand was batting that afternoon, and doing rather well. The chaste pavilions appeared not to notice. But The Hill around us was already rolling with noise, with cries of protest, throaty advice and challenge.

Having picked a comparatively bare spot half-way up the slope, it soon became clear to us that we were in a sort of no-man's-land between two opposing forces – New Zealand would send up a tidal cheer from their men to meet a counter-jeer crashing down from behind. About a quarter of an hour before the stumps, trouble began. The afternoon had been long and hot. The New Zealand side had done rather too well; and worse, supplies of beer had run out. Every man was now squatting on a cairn of crumpled empties, his face sweating with thirst and emotion. Suddenly they all got to their feet, picked up their cans and bottles, and began hurling them spitefully at one another.

'Don't like the look of this,' said my brother to the Archbishop's son, and they put their heads down between their knees. Missiles were now whistling in all directions, and tinkling and thumping on the ground all round. Caught as we were in midfire, I felt in a favoured position, and began to watch the battle with my head well up. Barrage and counter-barrage criss-crossed above me, seeming to go in waves as the men gathered fresh ammunition. Then looking down for a moment I saw large drops of blood falling on to my 'Somerset-Maugham' white tropical suiting.

'That's rich-looking blood,' I thought; then realized it was my own. I'd been clobbered on the head by a beer bottle. I felt no pain, but from this small flesh wound I bled like a slaughtered calf. No one around me seemed to have been similarly damaged, so I lay back and made the most of it. My white suit showed up the blood

to some advantage, and I was soon surrounded by an admiring
crowd.

'Now see what you've done. Hell, he looks bad, don't 'e?
Reckon he's dyin'? Better call a doctor.'

The battle was over, and the cricket-watchers calmed down.
The sight of blood made them contrite as children. There was
anxious sympathy all round, and maybe I overdid it, for suddenly I
was being given the kiss of life by a policeman. I broke free from
this and fell into the soft cotton-clothed arms of some young
student nurses from Adelaide, who held my wound closed with
their long scented fingers till the more proper bandages arrived.

Getting blooded on The Hill at Sydney cricket ground has
always struck me as something of a rare privilege for a foreigner.
It was a badge of both the passion and remorse of the cricket-
watching fraternity of Sydney, and later made me many friends in
bars of that city.

MILITARY MATTER

BY SIMON RAVEN (1982)

Simon Raven (1927–2001) was a novelist, playwright and journalist, best known for his hilarious portrayal of the mid-twentieth-century English upper classes. Educated first at Charterhouse, where he was introduced to the glorious game, and then at Cambridge, he later became a regular army officer serving in Germany and Kenya.

* * *

WHENEVER I REVIEW THE DAYS WHICH I PASSED AS A SOLDIER, I am always slightly shocked to recall how many of the least edifying or dignified scenes in which I took part were somehow connected with cricket, whether during play itself or the social aftermath. There was the shame-making time when an exigent demand from a bookmaker was served on me actually at the wicket, while I was batting for the Regiment in front of the Colonel-in-Chief and a Field-Marshal; or there was the derisory occasion in Berlin at which a two-innings match against the King's Own Yorkshire Light Infantry had to be converted in to a three- and then a four-innings match (so incompetent or 'tired' were the batsmen on either side) in order to provide some sort of spectacle for the visitors invited to meals or drinks on the ground during the two days allotted. For students of human oddity, however, a history which may have a more subtle appeal is the Very Strange Case of Major-General Frothbury . . .

One day in Kenya in the autumn of 1955 my Regiment fielded an Eleven against the Nairobi Club for a whole day's match on the latter's ground, which adjoined the commodious club-house. Our own team consisted almost entirely of officers who had been

brought down into Nairobi from their distant and isolated
companies in the Aberdare mountains especially for the occasion.
The logistic extravagance entailed was entirely justified, it appeared,
by the importance of the match, which was in fact a ponderous
exercise in public relations between the Regiment and the Colonial
Service, the Nairobi Club side being largely made up of district
officers or commissioners, with a sprinkling of Kenya policemen.
There were, in consequence, many spectators of high rank or
sycophantic inclination, among them Major-General Frothbury.

As there were no official umpires for the match, competent
volunteers from the audience took shifts of an hour or so, and
eventually, late in the afternoon, Frothbury expressed a genial wish
to take a turn. It was assumed by all, and asserted by his
demeanour, that he had at least adequate knowledge of the Laws of
Cricket, and after five staff officers had struggled for the honour of
helping him into the white coat he
duly took post at the 'Club end' of
the wicket.

The state of the game was
delicate. The Nairobi Club had
declared at 3.30 for 232 runs,
leaving us until 7 p.m. (three
hours, if we allow for the break
between innings and a brief
tea interval) to beat this total.
Although the fast outfield was in
our favour, we had none of us had
much practice at playing on matting
wickets, and the Nairobi club
bowling was reputed to be very
tight. By 5.30, when Frothbury
strutted on to the ground to
umpire, we had 121 for 5,
which put us well up with the

clock but otherwise in bad case, as the two men now at the wicket were our last two batsmen of substance, and once they were out the enemy would be right into our tail. One of them was a young National Service subaltern called Kenyon, a correct and neat player without, however, much power behind his strokes; the other was the only non-commissioned chap on our side, a certain Sergeant Jellico, whose brisk natural talent was marred by an unorthodox grip (left hand at the top of the handle and right hand rammed down on to the shoulders of the bat).

General Frothbury proceeded to take against both of them. As Kenyon told me afterwards, when they were at the bowling end together Frothbury would make remarks like 'Get on with it, will you, and stop finicking about', regardless of Kenyon's clear tactical duty as anchor-man, which was not 'to get on with it' but to stay put, and also regardless of the regulation which forbids the umpire to advise or rebuke the players save only in respect of the Laws. Sergeant Jellico received more conspicuous treatment: the General took his bat from him and demonstrated the orthodox grip. When the Sergeant, unrepentant, continued to use his own, the General put on an affronted scowl which deepened and darkened when Jellico drove two balls in succession for four and slammed the last of the over past deep mid-wicket for three. This meant that Jellico must now face the first ball of the next over, which would be bowled from Frothbury's end. The first ball the Sergeant received, a real sod as Kenyon said later, narrowly missed his off-stump.

'I told him about his grip,' said Frothbury to Kenyon. 'If he gets himself out he's no one to blame but himself.'

'I think he's had it too long to change, sir,' said Kenyon.

'Nonsense. Too swollen-headed to take advice. What's his name?'

Kenyon told him.

'Jellico,' said the General, storing it away. 'Nothing I hate more than a conceited NCO.'

The second ball of the over was far less savage and was

propelled in a huge arc over the bowler's head for six. The third
was swept away off the leg-stump, dangerously but effectively, for
four. Frothbury's face worked in discontent. The fourth was
slashed hissing towards cover but must, as it seemed, pass wide and
to his left.

'Come on, sir,' Jellico called.

Both batsmen started for the run; but before they had taken
two strides cover had miraculously gathered the ball with his left
hand.

'BACK,' shouted Jellico. He stopped dead and dived back
towards his crease. But for Kenyon it was much harder to stop. He
had been backing up properly as the ball was bowled and was
therefore going at a much greater momentum than Jellico. However,
he juddered to a halt and turned . . . too late, as cover-point had
flipped the ball straight back to the bowler, who crisply broke the
wicket.

'How's that?' the bowler said.

'Out,' said the General.

Kenyon began to walk.

'Not you,' said Frothbury. 'The other man, Sergeant Jellico.'

'But sir,' said Kenyon, 'the wicket was broken at my end.'

'The end to which he was running.'

'We hadn't crossed, sir,' said Kenyon, and continued on his
way.

'You come back here,' yapped the General, while Kenyon, a
decent but feeble young man, started to dither.

The captain of the Nairobi Club XI now walked up to
Frothbury and said, very pleasantly, 'Slight misunderstanding,
General. Often tricky, this kind of thing. But the non-striker's
wicket was broken, and since the batsmen hadn't crossed...'

'It's me,' said Kenyon, trying to be firm, 'that's out.'

He turned and marched away.

'YOU COME BACK,' squealed the General like an electric
saw. And then, to the Nairobi Club captain: 'Just teaching that

sergeant a lesson. He called the run, then he funked it. He should have kept straight on and let young Kenyon get to his end. Anyway, he needs pulling down a peg.'

The Nairobi Club captain smiled a ghastly smile and took a deep breath.

'I'm afraid that has nothing to do with it, sir. The Laws of Cricket state . . .'

'. . . That the umpire's decision is final,' snapped Frothbury, who was not a General for nothing. 'You come back here, Kenyon. Sergeant Jellico is out.'

The Nairobi Club captain beckoned wearily to the other umpire – a GSO II in Frothbury's headquarters, who cravenly deposed that his attention had been distracted by a mosquito and that he had missed the incident altogether.

It was at this stage that somebody at last behaved rather well. Sergeant Jellico, realizing that unless the General had his will there would be no more cricket that day, strode from the wicket looking neither to right nor to left but (so the loungers under the fans of the pavilion bar subsequently asserted) blinking very slightly with disappointment, for after all he had been batting with zest and valour and might well have won us the match.

From CRICKET WALLAH

BY SCYLD BERRY (1982)

Scyld Berry is a sports journalist of many years' standing, having
written for among other publications the *Sunday Telegraph*, *The
Observer* and *Wisden Cricket Monthly*. He has also written several
books, including *Cricket Wallah* (1982), from which the following
account is taken, and *A Cricket Odyssey* (1988).

* * *

BOTHAM'S FASTEST HUNDRED

THE NEHRU STADIUM AT INDORE IS TYPICAL OF THE GROUNDS ON
which England played outside the Test matches. A multi-
purpose stadium, it was built with government funds in the early
1960s in order to replace the old sports ground attached to the
Raj's principal social club. The same is the pattern throughout
India. The private ground that belonged to the British and native
elite, where other members of the public were allowed in as much
on sufferance as on payment to watch the big matches, has been
superseded by a new stadium for the many. It is a transformation
which might not be regrettable at all, were not the old grounds
such verdant, restful havens of retreat, like country-house estates
amid the dust of cities: the Bombay Gymkhana, the Roshanara
Club in Delhi, the Poona Club, and in Indore the Yeshwant Club,
named after the last Maharajah of Holkar. Some of these clubs
have become sad old places, going to seed as gently and
imperceptibly as the prince drinking to his memories at the club
bar. The paint and whitewash haven't been touched since 1947;
photographs and the billiard table grow dustier year by year . . .

Two elements, however, about this Nehru Stadium were

distinctive when Ian Botham staged the most outstanding innings
of the tour there. One was the statue outside the main entrance.
Made of stone and inscribed in Hindi, it aims to immortalize the
GOM of Indian cricket, Colonel C. K. Nayudu. In the time of the
old princely state of Holkar, Nayudu *was* Indore cricket. Crowds
would follow him down the street. He was the first Indian cricketer
to have charisma in the eyes of his own people (whereas Ranji had
been all the rage in England). His physical toughness is a legend:
once he was hit in the mouth by Dattu Phadkar; he swept two of
his front teeth off the pitch and carried on batting. Botham did
likewise when hit by Andy Roberts during his first season in the
Somerset side. Nayudu, having been trained on the erratic surface
of coir matting, lived adventurously as a batsman in search of
sixes; so does Botham. When Nayudu faced foreign bowling for
the first time, that of MCC in 1926, he hit it for 153, including 11
sixes, in 115 minutes. The statue to his memory, a fine one as
cricket art goes, does not by all accounts capture him in a
characteristic pose: C. K. is allowing a ball to pass by his off
stump. But it serves as a reminder of the presiding genius of
Indore.

A second peculiarity about the game was that when Botham
walked to the wicket on Friday 22 January it was the first time
since the tour began over two months before that England had not
been watched by a virtual capacity crowd. The Nehru Stadium was
less than half full, with barely 10,000 spread out around the
terracing. Local officials advanced the reasonable explanation that
the succession of four drawn Test matches had taken its toll of
spectator interest. Thus there was no great clamour of expectation
when Botham went in. A striped squirrel sat on top of the
sightscreen undisturbed. The surroundings were relaxed. So was
he; and he had already made the promise that he would hit.

When Botham walked out to bat thirty-five minutes after
lunch, at 1.25, England had just lost two wickets with their score
on 87, as if to prove it was one of the game's misfortunate

numbers. Geoff Cook, urgently needing plenty of runs if he was going to make the Test side in Kanpur, had been caught at midwicket for 39; or so the umpire decided. The fielder Sanjeeva Rao had dived forward at the ball, and the batsman clearly believed he had picked it up on the half-volley. Cook, however, apart from waiting in his crease for the decision, made no sign of dissent, although his partner, Fletcher, shrugged his shoulders and pointed at Rao with his bat. After an idle morning the game had sprung alive. With no run added, Fletcher drove an off break from Gopal Sharma to mid-on, who dropped it. At the next ball Fletcher cut and was caught by the wicketkeeper, who for good measure also knocked off the bails.

Picking up his 2lb 12oz bat and jamming on his sunhat, Botham called out to the next man in after him, Taylor, 'You'd better get ready.' On his way to the wicket he had no need to look up at the sun because the sky was its usual cloudless self. He could see in front of him, beyond the stadium, a six-storey hospital donated by the former Maharajah of Holkar. Beside it was the old medical college, with a couple of red-tiled turrets that would not have been out of place in Oxford, next to Keble. To his right through some trees was the squat tower of a brightly whitewashed church: that of St Ann's, built in thanksgiving for the suppression of the Mutiny. The plaques inside still poignantly commemorate: Captain Francis Brodie, Commandant of Cavalry, Malwa Contingent, 'killed by Mutineers at Mulharghur on June 12th 1857 whilst in the fearless discharge of his duty'; Ross MacMahon esquire, Civil Engineer . . . 'whose valuable life in its very prime was cut short in the outbreak at Indore on July 1st 1857'. But not all those commemorated were casualties of war. There is also a plaque to one 'who died from the Effects of a Fall at Polo, aged 29. Erected by his brother officers of the Central Indian Horse'. A cavalier: that is more Botham's style.

He began by playing out the two deliveries remaining of the over by Gopal Sharma, a manifestly keen young off-spinner who

had been included in India's twelve for the Madras and Kanpur
Tests. At the other end was Gatting, who had replaced Cook and
had yet to get off the mark. Bent on a good score to make sure of
his place in Kanpur, Gatting saw out a maiden over from Anil
Mathur, a left-arm medium-pacer who had swung the new ball
sharply and had returned for a second spell at the main-stand end.
Each batsman opened his account with a single in Sharma's next
over; then Botham unleashed an off drive that sent the ball
skidding through mid-off for four. From this stroke it was obvious,
as it had not been before during England's hesitant start, that the
outfield was exceptionally quick. Constant games of football and
hockey on it, combined with a local scarcity of water, had reduced
all but a few tufts to hard-baked earth. Ten runs to Botham off
that over, followed by another five off Mathur, confirmed
impressions that the going was good, the pitch ideal in pace and
bounce, and the batsman intent on belligerence.

Then Botham made the first of only two serious mistakes.
Trying to cut Sharma he was dropped by slip, who also could not
quite reach the rebound. With 15 to his name at that stage, Botham
played out the rest of the over for a circumspect maiden. Thus
Botham and Gatting, in their partnership of 137 off 12.2 overs,
could afford to allow two of them to be maidens.

In the following over from Mathur, Botham stepped down the
pitch and lofted the ball far above the height of St Ann's tower,
more to that of a steeple. It was like his shot at Old Trafford
against Terry Alderman the previous summer, when he was nearly
caught from the skyer to end all skyers by mid-off running
desperately back ('I got my angles wrong'); this time too the ball
went up even further than it carried. Nonetheless it went for six, a
few feet to the on-side of straight. Fifteen runs off Mathur's over
took Botham's score to 30. Whereupon drinks were brought out,
to account for almost five of his fifty-five minutes at the wicket.
Botham drank some of the green 'staminade', and repeated the
message that the next batsman should be ready to come in any

minute.

He did not feel so hot as to remove his sleeveless MCC sweater. Yet the day was warm, though fresh because of Indore's altitude of 1,800 feet; and he was about to perform one of the great feats of hitting. He cut the first ball he received after the drinks interval – an off break from Sharma – to the third-man boundary, off-drove the second for four more and swept the third for six. Like all his sixes it was a minimum seventy-five-yard carry. Off the fourth ball he pushed (in anyone else's parlance 'drove') another single; but here he may have miscalculated as the first ball had been a no-ball, which left Gatting with three balls of the over to play out.

With Botham now on 45, the Central Zone captain Parthasarathy Sharma decided on a bowling change. Removing Mathur from the firing line, Sharma brought on a left-arm spinner, Rajinder Singh Hans, at the main-stand end. Hans was once rated a potential successor to his fellow Sikh Bedi. But his bowling, at least in this match, was poor in direction and suffered from a scrambling delivery. Hans ran up and pushed the ball through enthusiastically: Botham reverse-swept him for four. A single from the next ball brought up Botham's fifty. Given the strike again one ball later, he hit Hans over extra cover for six, then pinched the strike with a single: 61.

At the far, hospital end, Gopal Sharma was still spinning the ball sufficiently to make it drift in the air away from the batsman and maybe turning it, except that Botham had dispatched it towards the boundary long before it had any chance to turn. He swung the first ball of his new over for two, and reverse-swept the next for four more. At the other end Gatting laughed in his beard. His mind went back to the one-day international in Ahmadabad, when he had shared a match-winning partnership with Botham. The joint plan then, as proposed by Botham on his arrival, had been to push the ball around and steadily accumulate the 31 runs required. Thereupon, far from suiting his action to the word,

Botham had reverse-swept Doshi and hit two sixes over long on. Now here he was again cheerfully breaking all conventions, but so monstrously gifted he was getting away with it. So Gatting contented himself with giving Botham his head and the strike, which the latter was in any event so intent on keeping that once during this over, after scoring a two, he ran thirty yards past his stumps lest he be called for a third.

Botham, his score 70 when Hans began a new over, made the second of his mistakes when he came down the pitch to the first ball and missed it. So did the wicketkeeper, Ved Raj, as it 'went with the arm' and shot past leg stump for four byes. Nothing daunted, Botham swung a four to square leg and half-mowed, half-carted the next ball for his fourth six, falling away to leg as he did so. It pitched around leg stump and kept going, first with the bowler's arm, then with the bat. At this point Hans, as a Sikh, might have remembered that he carried a dagger with him to deal with just such an attack.

And the fielders all this while? Faced with this hectic activity both on the field and scoreboard (which was forced to confine itself to registering the tens and forgetting about the digits), they remained enthusiastic, if within certain limits. They did not dive after the balls because it is not the Indian custom to dive on hard bare outfields. But if retrieving the ball from the wire fence around the boundary was their primary function, this they did well.

One fielder, however, made the elementary mistake of straying in a few yards from the boundary at long off when Sharma the captain tried his own occasional off breaks instead of Gopal Sharma's. Botham sent the first ball like a tracer bullet to where long off should have been, only to land safely over the line for six more (safely for the fielder perhaps more so than for Botham). Sharma's next rather stiff and portly off break was swung away to square leg, where two fielders stood politely back to allow each other the honour of catching it; four more. These two incidents apart, the Central Zone fielding was by no means as poor as it might have been under the assault. A cut for two and another single took Botham to 94.

When Botham embarked upon the next over from Hans, the only unexpected feature of it was that he did not reach his century with a six. He certainly tried to by stepping inside a leg-stump ball in order to swing it over square leg, but it took the bottom edge and ran down to fine leg for a mere four. Botham 98, and the next ball was identical in both its delivery and dispatch. Botham therefore had reached his hundred off the forty-eighth delivery he had received. Only Robin Hobbs and Lance Cairns are *known* to have reached three figures off fewer deliveries in a first-class match: 45 in both cases. Two centuries by Gilbert Jessop may have been quicker still, but that is conjecture; and with early scorebooks lost the matter can never be verified. In terms of time Botham had taken 50 minutes. That put him into equal tenth place among the fastest century-makers (and at least two of those above him had not made their runs in serious circumstances). The drinks interval too had wasted several minutes for him.

If there was any scope left for Botham to open out, he did so immediately on reaching his century. He drove the third ball of Hans's over to long on for six, and heaved the fourth over square leg for another six, his seventh. Hans, shifting his line, pushed his fifth ball through on off stump but Botham stepped back, drove, and with a huge grin sliced it through the absent slips for four more. Twenty-four runs had come off the over so far; Botham might have made it 30, but tried instead to keep the strike by pushing a single on the off side. The ball, however, struck his pad, and the keeper was too quick for him to scuttle through for a leg bye. To this point, off the last seven overs, Botham had personally scored 103.

Gatting meanwhile had done his supporting role immaculately by scoring three singles, to Botham's 118 in all. Then he too hit Sharma the captain for a six over long on, prompting Botham to clap him, not in any way sarcastically. A single to Gatting left

Botham with three more balls to face: another four, a miss, and finally a pull drive which sent the ball suitably far into the stratosphere before it descended into deep midwicket's hands. As he walked off, the Nehru Stadium rose. Gatting led the applause of every player on the field. Suddenly, as Botham reached the edge of the playing area, a piece of orange peel landed and rolled towards him. But even that he scooped up and hit away with his bat, bang off the middle. And he was still wearing his sweater.

Gatting afterwards rated it 'a great, great innings' and thought Botham would never surpass it because 'in England the bowlers would be familiar with him, and anywhere else the fielders are going to be a bit keener'. Underwood, amazed, said that a bowler had to attack Botham's stumps 'but even when he mistimes the ball it could still go for six because he hits the thing so hard'. Willis, however, whose sardonic exterior could not quite disguise his admiration, felt that Botham could exceed even this effort. 'The Megastar,' he grunted, 'he could do anything, within the next four to five years.'

Nayudu was born in Nagpur on 31 October 1895, so he was already thirty-one by the time he had his first taste of any international cricket. At the age of fifty he made 200 in a first-class match. At the age of sixty-one he was asked to come out of retirement to assist Uttar Pradesh in a Ranji Trophy match against Rajasthan. The Rajasthan attack included Ramchand and Mankad, proven Test bowlers both; but Nayudu still agreed. The story is concluded by Raj Singh Dungapore, who captained Rajasthan in that match:

> The Old Man came in when his side had lost four cheap wickets and Vinoo Mankad was bowling. Now there had always been rivalry between them. It was Vinoo who had suggested to Phadkar that he bowl the bouncer which hit C. K. in the mouth. And in 1952 Mankad had been refused a tour guarantee by C. K., then chairman of selectors,

which resulted in Mankad not being a member of the touring party to England.

Vinoo's first ball to the Old Man came in with the arm and had him absolutely plumb leg before, except that the umpire wouldn't give him out. Second ball Vinoo was so furious he bowled a beamer which nearly took the Old Man's head off and went for four byes. Third ball he pitched up and C. K. swung him away for six; Vinoo just stood there and glared, and the Old Man stood there too, his back ramrod straight as it was until the end of his life. Fourth ball C. K. again swung him away for six, another seven-iron shot. He made 84 that day before he was run out, after he had dropped his bat going for a third run.

At sixty-one – and there is no doubt about his age – Nayudu's has to be one of the most remarkable innings in first-class cricket. If Botham seeks more challenges in later life, he would do well to surpass that in the year 2016.

From CHATS ON THE CRICKET FIELD

BY W. A. BETTESWORTH (1910)

KING GEORGE THE FOURTH, WHEN RIDING IN THE GREAT PARK, AT Windsor, once came across a large party of his domestics playing the game near the Lodge. At the unexpected approach of the King the servants began to scamper in all directions, but His Majesty, much amused, sent one of the gentlemen in attendance to desire them to continue their game, and never to let his approach interrupt their sports. The King then continued his ride in another direction, observing in his attendants that cricket was a noble game, and that when he used to play cricket he enjoyed it as much as anyone.

From THE GENTLEMAN'S MAGAZINE

BY THE REV. JOHN MITFORD (1833)

WE MUST HASTEN ON, FOR WE ARE AT LENGTH ARRIVED AT THE tent of *Achilles* himself. Stop, reader, and look, if thou art a cricketer, with reverence and awe on that venerable and aged form! These are the remains of the once great, glorious, and unrivalled William Beldham, called for love and respect, and for his flaxen locks and his fair complexion, 'Silver Billy'. Beldham was a close-set, active man, about five feet eight inches. Never was such a player! So safe, so brilliant, so quick, so circumspect; so able in counsel, so active in the field; in deliberation so judicious, in execution so tremendous. It mattered not to him who bowled, or how he bowled, fast or slow, high or low, straight or bias; away flew the ball from his bat, like an eagle on the wing.

It was a study for Phidias to see Beldham rise to strike; the grandeur of the attitude, the settled composure of the look, the piercing lightening of the eye, the rapid glance of the bat, were electrical. Men's hearts throbbed within them, their cheeks turned pale and red. Michelangelo should have painted him. Beldham was great in every hit, but his peculiar glory was the *cut*. Here he stood with no man beside him, the laurel was all his own; it was like the cut of a *racket*. His wrist seemed to turn on springs of the finest steel. He took the ball, as Burke did the House of Commons, between wind and water; not a moment too soon or too late. Beldham still survives. He lives near Farnham; and in his kitchen, black with age, but, like himself, still untouched with worms, hangs the trophy of his victories, the delight of his youth, the exercise of his manhood, and the glory of his age – his BAT. Reader! believe me, when I tell you I trembled when I touched it; it seemed an act of profaneness, of violation. I pressed it to my lips, and returned it to its sanctuary.

BALLADE OF DEAD CRICKETERS

BY ANDREW LANG (1884)

Ah, where be Beldham now, and Brett,
　　Barker, and Hogsflesh, where be they?
Brett, of all bowlers fleetest yet
　　That drove the bails in disarray?
And Small that would, like Orpheus, play
　　Till wild bulls followed his minstrelsy?
Booker, and Quiddington, and May?
　　Beneath the daisies, there they lie!

And where is Lambert, that would get
　　The stumps with balls that broke astray?
And Mann, whose balls would ricochet
　　In almost an unholy way
(So do baseballers 'pitch' today);
　　George Leer, that seldom let a bye,
And Richard Nyren, grave and gray?
　　Beneath the daisies, there they lie!

Tom Sueter, too, the ladies' pet,
　　Brown that would bravest hearts affray;
Walker, invincible when set,
　　(Tom, of the spider limbs and splay);
Think ye that we could match them, pray,
　　These heroes of Broad-halfpenny,
With Buck to hit, and Small to Stay?
　　Beneath the daisies, there they lie!

Envoy
Prince, canst thou moralize the lay?
　　How all things change below the sky?
Of Fry and Hirst shall mortals say,
　　'Beneath the daisies, there they lie!'

From THE ADVENTURES OF
MR VERDANT GREEN
(AN OXFORD FRESHMAN)

BY CUTHBERT BEDE (1911)

AS HE HAD FULLY EQUIPPED HIMSELF FOR ARCHERY, SO ALSO MR Verdant Green (on the authority of Mr Bouncer) got himself up for cricket regardless of expense; and he made his first appearance in the field in a straw hat with blue ribbon, and 'flannels', and spiked shoes of perfect propriety. As Mr Bouncer had told him that, in cricket, attitude was everything, Verdant, as soon as he went in for his innings, took up what he considered to be a very good position at the wicket. Little Mr Bouncer, who was bowling, delivered the ball with a swiftness that seemed rather astonishing in such a small gentleman.

The first ball was 'wide'; nevertheless, Verdant (after it had passed) struck at it, raising his bat high in the air, and bringing it straight down to the ground as though it were an executioner's axe. The second ball was nearer to the mark, but it came in with such a swiftness, that, as Mr Verdant Green was quite new to round bowling, it was rather too quick for him, and hit him severely on the –, well never mind – on the trousers.

'Hallo, Gig-lamps!' shouted the delighted Mr Bouncer, 'nothing like backing up; but it's no use assuming a stern appearance; you'll get your hand in soon, old feller!'

But Verdant found that before he could get his hand in, the ball was got into his wicket; and that while he was preparing for the strike, the ball shot by; and, as Mr Stumps, the wicket-keeper, kindly informed him, 'there was a row in his timber-yard'. Thus Verdant's score was always on the *lucas a non lucendo* principle of derivation, for not even to a quarter of a score did it ever reach; and he felt that he should never rival a Mynn or be a Parr with any one of the 'All England' players.

From AT THE SIGN OF THE WICKET

BY E. B. V. CHRISTIAN (1894)

THERE IS ALWAYS A SENSE OF SADNESS ABOUT THE DRAWING OF THE stumps. Standing alone upon the Heath, filled an hour ago with a crowd of excited people, now deserted by all but the workmen taking down the tent, hearing the voices of the players departing in twos and threes dying away in the lanes as the stars come out, you feel the very air breathe a chastened melancholy. But at the end of the season it is doubly sad. To know that the last ball is bowled, the last run made – 'tears inhibit my tongue' as I think of it. Before next season a hundred changes may have happened. The goodly fellowship of our eleven may never meet again unbroken; the calls of business – or that louder call – will have taken some, at least, away. And one change is already determined on, to me as serious almost as any could be. We have played our last match on the Heath. We finished the season gloriously just now, beating the Shalford men after a close match by three wickets; and when Old Martin, our umpire, drew the stumps and walked gravely to the tent, the last game upon the old Heath was ended; the scene of a thousand pleasant contests will see us no more.

I protest I feel a choky sensation as I write it, but it is true. The turf, they said, is bad; the furze grows too near; they urged a hundred trifles such as these in favour of the change. The real reason, I believe, is that the mile walk from the village across the Park deters some spectators, and even some lazy players, from coming up. And they are going instead to the new Playing Fields close to the village. The turf there may be as good, the out-fielding a little better, but to me the change is bitterness and vexation of spirit. To break the old associations; to get no more fours up to the Park palings, no more late cuts up to the window where my cousin Frank sits watching us from his invalid chair; to turn no more to look at the clouds rising over the firwoods, or to note between the overs the Peaslake mill standing clear against the August sky – this to me will be like losing an arm.

From THE CRICKET MATCH

BY HUGH DE SELINCOURT (1924)

Hugh de Selincourt (1878–1951) wrote several books including *Oxford from Within* (1910), *The Game of the Season* (1931) and *The Saturday Match* (1937). In the extract below he records the epic village match between Tillingford and Raveley. I think you'll agree it makes for the perfect ending to this anthology.

* * *

THE EVENING PASSES AND NIGHT FALLS

I

THE STUMPS HAD BEEN PULLED UP AND STORED WITH THE UMPIRE'S torn coats in the locker; the seats and benches had been carried into the pavilion; the large shutters had been lowered; the doors of the pavilion barred and locked. The cricket ground, in the light of the sinking sun, looked as desolate as the two worn patches by the bowler's creases, which were now the only visible signs that a match had been played.

Players and spectators straggled up the road to the village in thick gossiping throngs, through which young Trine in his two-

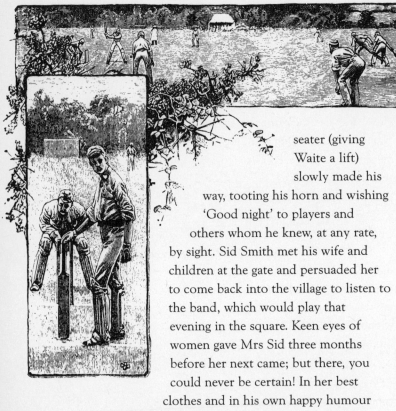

seater (giving Waite a lift) slowly made his way, tooting his horn and wishing 'Good night' to players and others whom he knew, at any rate, by sight. Sid Smith met his wife and children at the gate and persuaded her to come back into the village to listen to the band, which would play that evening in the square. Keen eyes of women gave Mrs Sid three months before her next came; but there, you could never be certain! In her best clothes and in his own happy humour after the match Sid had a glimpse of the fine lass, Liz, he had wooed before the swamp of domesticity had closed over their heads. He pushed the perambulator up the hill in the vain but valiant hope of regaining that girl, a hope that glimmered dimly and dumbly in some remote corner of his consciousness.

Old John, Ted Bannister and Teddie White slowed up as they came to the Dog and Duck. Old John in a more benevolent mood even than usual, was much affected by the sight of the small family party, Sid pushing the pram, with two small boys hanging on to his jacket. He came hurrying up to Mrs Smith.

'You must let your husband join us,' he said. 'We've had such a glorious nice match; the best match as I've ever played in, I do verily believe.'

All smiles, Mrs Sid answered, 'Now, don't you keep him long, Mr McLeod, mind.'

'Long, bless me, no, Mrs Smith! But your good man'll be parched as a day in the desert.'

'Oh no! That's all right; I'll stay here,' said Sid, protesting. But Ted Bannister took one arm and old John the other, and he was dragged into the Dog and Duck, not, it must be owned, too reluctantly. A friendly but vigorous argument ensued between John and Ted Bannister as to who should stand treat, which was won by Ted Bannister, John grumbling that he never knew such a chap.

'Go on, put that inside yourself, mate,' said Ted, handing him a pint of old Burton, for which the Dog and Duck had a name.

Nothing is quite so refreshing as a long, cool drink of good old ale after a hot afternoon's cricket; each man took a long, appreciative draught after wishing each other, 'Well, here's luck!' and then in silence allowed the pleasant effect of that drink to permeate quietly through him before enjoying another good pull at the big pewter mug. John's face was a study of happy comfort as he slowly tilted his pot and, emptying it, set it down on the counter, carefully drawing a deep, comfortable sigh. Beaming, he watched the others follow his excellent example and then said, as though inspired by a sudden novel idea of extreme brilliancy:

'How about another small one?'

The men smiled. In a most businesslike manner John asked Jock, the barman, for another half-pint each, and over that the men, their first parched thirst quenched, were able to chat. They discussed the great question who had really done most to win the match for Tillingfold, and after dismissing the claims, first of one man, then of another, came to the conclusion that every man on the side had done his share.

'Ah, that's the beauty of cricket!' declared Old John heartily, wiping his face all over with a large handkerchief. 'That's the glorious beauty of cricket! Every single man-jack of us helped, one way or another, to win that game.'

'Yes!' said Ted Bannister, with the utmost composure. 'If there is a better game than cricket I should like to know it.' And he surveyed the company as a man does who has said the last word.

What would have been Gauvinier's thoughts had he heard him say it?

II

Gauvinier, as a matter of fact, was quietly absorbing with Francis Allen, the scorer, a tap of old beer which he preferred to that to be obtained at the Dog and Duck. The pub was at the end of the village, more retired perhaps and secluded.

'It adds to the life of the place, a game like that, this afternoon,' said Gauvinier. 'It'll be a pity if we can't get another field for football and cricket should have to stop. The turf must have a rest.'

'Yes, it's just got going proper-like since the war.'

'All the grousing and chat really is only a sign of keenness, don't you think?'

'No use payin' any heed to that, man,' said old Francis encouragingly, pouring his beer down.

'I wonder why one is so mad on cricket. It's only a game, after all.'

'Here, you'd better have another half-pint to wash that duck of yours off your chest.'

He ordered it, while Paul laughed.

'I'd like to have made a few today. Your young Horace batted well. He should be a fine cricketer one day.'

'They're nice people, the whole lot of 'em,' said Francis appreciatively. 'The nipper wanted to play today – just a little. I had some fun with 'un this morning.' He paused, savouring the reminiscence. 'Wouldn't let on I had a message for 'un. He pretty nigh bust hisself wanting to know.'

'The kid's not an atom conceited. I'd as soon have him on a side as any man I've ever played with.'

Francis looked very pleased. 'Except, perhaps, Mr Waite, eh? or Ted Bannister?' he slyly suggested.

'You are an old devil. Who's ever told you…'

'Who's told me! You hide yer blummin' feelings too well.'

'Oh, damn it! I try to,' said Gauvinier guiltily. 'But that catch…' He began to shake with laughter.

'Pretty near scared the life out of him! Mind now, or you'll spill the beer over your trousies. I could see his scared look from the score-box.'

Gauvinier managed to finish his beer without a catastrophe. 'The joke is that half Tillingfold will think him a class fielder now.'

'Well, why not?'

'Oh, no reason, of course, only it's rather funny. So damnably like the world.'

'It takes all sorts to make a world, if it comes to that.'

'You're right, Francis, you're right. One's little job is to find the place for the Bannocks and the Bannisters, that's all.'

There was a silence.

'Oh well,' said Gauvinier, 'I must push along, I suppose.'

'Yes, mustn't sit here all the evening makin' beasts of ourselves.'

They slowly 'got a move on', and Gauvinier mounted his bicycle and rode home into the glory of the evening. Even the cricket match was forgotten for a while as he looked at the blaze of colour which celebrated the close of the day. He rode slowly, lingering as at a majestic rite. The whole vast sky glowed red and orange; the trees shone rosy in the reflected light which touched the hills. No breath of wind stirred the glowing stillness. His heart worshipped God and colour and life. And night was treading softly from the woods where the little owls were beginning to cry.